*Particle Size:*
**Measurement, Interpretation, and Application**

# Particle Size: Measurement, Interpretation, and Application

*Riyad R. Irani and Clayton F. Callis*

Monsanto Chemical Company, St. Louis, Missouri

**John Wiley & Sons, Inc., New York • London**

4594

# Preface

It seems clear to us that scientific progress depends on the development of better tools and better methods for measuring properties of materials. This general statement certainly applies to the very important property of finely divided matter, the particle size distribution.

There are many known examples of the dependence of the properties of materials on their particle size characteristics. This is amplified in Chapter 1, where a number of common applications of particle size distribution measurements are described.

Having gone through the process of equipping a laboratory with all the necessary tools for measuring particle size, it became clear to us that no single reference work existed which would give an analyst a simple choice of the preferred technique for particle size measurement of a specific material. The present book was written to fulfill this need, as well as to aid in the interpretation of the results.

The subject matter is inclusive and simplified to allow the novice to become familiar with the techniques, interpretation, and utility of particle sizing within a reasonable amount of time, yet simplification is not made at the expense of a rigorous treatment.

The order of the chapters is somewhat arbitrary. For those wanting to choose rapidly the appropriate method of particle size measurement, Chapters 10, 5, 6, 7, and 8 should be read in that order. Those investigators knowledgeable in particle size technology, but wanting to verify that they are proceeding correctly, should find the flow sheets in

Chapter 10 and the comparison of data from various techniques in Chapter 9 very useful.

Chapters 2 and 3 on definitions and methods of data presentation are of an introductory nature. Readers unfamiliar with the subject matter should study these chapters first. Chapter 4, on the mathematical treatment of particle size distribution, would be of interest to those wishing to delve deeply into the subject.

R. R. IRANI

C. F. CALLIS

*St. Louis, Mo.*
*March, 1963*

# Contents

*Particle Size:*
Measurement, Interpretation, and Application

# chapter 1

# Applications of particle size distribution measurements

The uses for materials in a finely divided form are astonishingly common and diverse. Around the home, such things as flour, salt, sugar, coffee, and face powder immediately come to mind. Other household products such as toothpaste, detergents, polishes, insecticides, drugs, and abrasives also contain a finely divided material as an essential component. Many industrial operations either handle or consume powders or produce a powder as the final product. The cement, glass, ceramic, paint, coal, fertilizer, food, paper, drug, dye, cosmetic, and even other industries perhaps, should be mentioned. Many natural phenomena result from the properties of matter in a finely divided state.

One of the most basic physical properties common to all these finely divided substances is their particle size distribution, that is, the frequency of occurrence of particles of every size present. The characteristics of a single particle are not usually of practical interest; rather, the mean characteristics of a large number of particles is the thing that can be studied statistically. It should be emphasized, however, that the knowledge of the size characteristics is of no value unless adequate correlation has been established with functional properties of specific interest or with processing variables that can be controlled.

Many investigations of the significance of particle size data are reported in the literature. Some of these reports are reviewed in this introductory chapter in order to point out more specifically, with detailed examples, the importance of this basic physical property in the

*1*

present-day technology of many common materials. No attempt has been made to present an all-comprehensive survey of these applications; in fact, some entire fields of investigation have been omitted, and, understandably, the interests of the authors are emphasized. The experiences described in this chapter should adequately demonstrate that when problems arise in the handling and use of finely divided materials, one of the first things that should be investigated is the particle size distribution, because more often than not this is a controlling factor.

The chapter is divided into two parts. The first part deals with applications of commercial interest, whereas the second part describes properties of particulate matter that are affected by particle size.

## COMMERCIAL APPLICATIONS INFLUENCED BY PARTICLE SIZE

### Segregation of Powdered Mixtures

Uniform mixtures of chemically different powders will be stable as regards segregation only if the powders are of similar particle size distributions. This is a significant practical problem in the fertilizer industry, where the "blender" is required by law in most areas not only to deliver the quantity of each plant food constituent claimed, but also to guarantee the lot to the purchaser as a uniform mixture. The primary mechanism of segregation in bulk fertilizers involves the differing tendencies of particles of varying size and shape to roll down an incline. Segregation occurs as the blended fertilizer is piled into a truck or bin if materials of widely varying particle sizes are present.

### Flow Conditioning

Dramatic changes in the physical properties of poor-flowing powdered and granular materials can often be effected by the addition of small amounts of finely divided powders. The additive is generally referred to as a flow-conditioning agent. An optimum conditioner level exists (1) for each conditioner-material system beyond which flow may not change significantly or may become poorer. Flowability at this level may be quite different for different conditioners.

Effective conditioning agents must adhere strongly to the surface of the material being conditioned and are much smaller in size. Microscopic examinations (2, 3) of conditioned material show that particles of the material are uniformly coated with particles of the conditioner. Figure 1-1 demonstrates the covering power of diatomaceous earth at the 2% level in a mixed fertilizer with an average particle size of 150 microns. The importance of the relative particle sizes of conditioner

(a)                                        (b)

FIG. 1-1. 150-micron particles of mixed fertilizer before (left) and after (right) addition of 2% diatomaceous earth.

and material is obvious from calculations of the number of particles of conditioner per particle of material. For example, with 1-micron conditioner and 20-micron material, this number is eighty. For 2-micron conditioner and the same material, the number drops to ten. The optimum concentration of flow conditioner is explainable (1) in terms of saturation of the material being conditioned, followed by formation of flocks of conditioner particles that retard over-all flow.

The flow properties of a powder can also be improved in many cases by mixing in coarser, free-flowing materials. The amount of coarser material needed to improve flow is generally exceedingly high, up to 1000% of the original powder. In these mixtures, the fines of the material being conditioned adhere to the surface of the large particles of flow-improving agent (4). It is interesting to note that this effect has been used (1, 5) as a basis of flow tests for measuring the flowability of powders.

## Cake Inhibition

The mechanism of caking has been fairly well established because of the considerable attention devoted to the problem by the fertilizer, salt, sugar and related industries (6–13). The presence of moisture, whether in the sample or artificially introduced, is necessary for caking to take place. The formation of a saturated solution on the particle

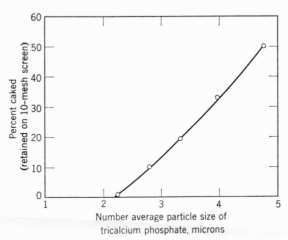

FIG. 1-2. Caking of milled salt when mixed with 1% tricalcium phosphate of different particle size. Reproduced from *Ind. Eng. Chem.,* **51**, 1288 (1959).

surfaces followed by evaporation of moisture from the solution leaves a residue that bridges and binds together the original particles.

The general considerations discussed for the flow-conditioning agents also apply to anticaking agents. The particle sizes of both the material and the anticaking agent are important. Hardesty and Kumagai (7) have shown that the more finely divided a mixed fertilizer the more severe the caking, whether an anticaking agent is present or not. They also report that large-particle conditioners are relatively ineffective. Irani, Callis, and Liu (1) measured the caking of samples of milled salt mixed with equal weights of tricalcium phosphate samples of different average particle sizes but approximately equally broad size distributions. They found that the finer the particle size of the conditioner, the less severe was the caking of the salt. This correlation is reproduced in Fig. 1-2. Other studies on fertilizers (12) have shown that the presence of a conditioner does not prevent formation of crystallite shells on particle surfaces but, in most cases, these shells are contained beneath the conditioner coating.

## Properties of Kaolinite

Regular variation in specific surface area, exchange capacity, heat of wetting, linear drying shrinkage, and permeability time of water leaching with particle size for kaolinite is reported by Harman and Fraulini (14). Numerical values of these properties for various size fractions are reported in Table 1-1.

### TABLE 1-1

#### Properties of Kaolinite (14) of Different Particle Sizes

| Size (microns) | Specific Surface (sq. m/gm) | Base Exchange Capacity (milliequiv./ 100 gm) | Permeability Time to Leach through Layer, 10 ml of Water (sec) | Heat of Wetting (cal/gm) | Linear Drying Shrinkage (% dry length) |
|---|---|---|---|---|---|
| 0.05–0.10 | 30.2 | 9.50 | 750.0 | — | — |
| 0.10–0.25 | 12.9 | 5.43 | 474.0 | 1.89 | 3.70 |
| 0.25–0.5 | 6.6 | 3.88 | 452.0 | 1.42 | 2.69 |
| 0.5–1 | 3.0 | 3.76 | 200.0 | 1.38 | 2.35 |
| 2–4 | 0.7 | 3.58 | 15.0 | 1.15 | 2.19 |
| 5–10 | 0.3 | 2.60 | 4.4 | 0.99 | 1.89 |
| 10–20 | 0.15 | 2.40 | 2.7 | 0.95 | 1.45 |

### Dust Explosions

Fine particles of various substances, when suspended in air, are explosive under certain conditions. Dusts vary widely in their inflammability because of differences in composition, concentration, and particle size (15). An increase in the inflammability of a given dust with increase in fineness has been observed from measurements of pressures generated on explosion (16) and from changes in inflammability on the addition of known percentages of inert dust such as fuller's earth (17).

### Surface Coverage of Pigments

Pigments are examined routinely for the presence of large particles or aggregates which may adversely affect texture, gloss, and opacity (18). Most of the well-produced micronized pigments contain no particles over 2–3 microns in size (19). The opacity of a paint is qualitatively found to be inversely proportional to the particle size of the pigment when the particles are larger than the wave length of light (20). Particles smaller than the wavelength of light scatter rather than reflect the light, with a possible resulting decrease in opacity. A minimum of white reflectance is desirable for the densest black pigments, and therefore the tendency is to reduce the particles of black pigments to sizes smaller than the wavelength of light.

A decrease in the particle size of calcium carbonate extender pigments has been found to improve the surface coverage, also known as hiding power, and gloss of a paint film (21), presumably from improvement in the dispersion of the hiding pigment by the very fine calcuim carbonate.

The shape of the particles of a pigment is apparently of considerable significance in the durability of paint films. Paints prepared from acicular-type zinc-oxide fillers have been shown to weather better than those compounded from other forms of the oxide of similar purity (22).

The significance of surface coverage in flow conditioning of solids has been mentioned earlier. Other examples where surface coverage is important include face powder, chalk, carbon for auto tires, and fillers for paper.

### Abrasiveness of Dental Polishing Agents

Dentifrices contain several ingredients, one of which is an abrasive solid whose function is removing debris and stains from the teeth and polishing the tooth surface (23). The abrasive used in tooth powders should be of such a particle size that dust will not be generated on handling, and yet small enough not to be gritty in the mouth. Studies of the influence of particle size of powders on their abrasiveness have been reported for calcium carbonate (24) and dicalcium phosphate (25). The abrasiveness of calcium carbonate powders was found to increase regularly with the respective weight average particle diameters (24). Epstein and Tainter (25) also concluded that the particle size of a powder is a reliable indication of its abrasiveness and suggest the use of slopes of curves relating median particle sizes to determined abrasiveness for comparing the abrasive power of different materials. According to this criterion, precipitated calcium carbonate is about six times as abrasive as dicalcium phosphate. The abrasive characteristics, however, are markedly influenced by other factors such as shape of particles, surface roughness differences, and the presence of impurities in the preparation. Empirical correlations of abrasiveness and particle size may vary for different materials and for different preparations of the same chemical.

### Atmospheric Contamination

Particle size studies of the nature of the particulate matter in smog-laden city atmospheres have shown that the material responsible for much of the decrease of visibility consists of particles having diameters of about the wavelength of light (26). In the City of Los Angeles, this material consists largely of hygroscopic droplets.

The human nose filters out almost all particles over 10 microns in size and about 95% of all particles greater than 5 microns from dust-polluted air (27). Silica particles about 0.5 micron in size seem to be particularly active in producing silicosis. Particles below 0.1 micron may be too small to be retained by the lungs (28), and particles below 5 microns in size can pass from the lungs to the blood and may reach the lymphatic system. These findings are of extreme importance, of course, in the design of filters to remove the particles from polluted air and prevent physiological damage.

Dustiness of a powdered material, a major nuisance in bulk handling and a source of air contamination, cannot be predicted solely on the basis of particle size information (29). A very important factor is the "stickiness" of the powder or how well the particles adhere to one another. With materials of broad size distributions, the very fine particles may coat the larger particles and hence not show up as dust (see flow conditioning). Andreasen et al. (29) state that for a given material removal of fines below 10 microns lowers the dustability.

### Behavior of Drugs

The particle sizes of drugs such as penicillin and streptomycin are rigidly controlled during manufacture (30). A small particle size allows more rapid resuspension into the medium following separation on storage and permits the use of small needles for injection. A lower limit, however, is imposed when local poisoning results from a too-rapid rate of dissolution into the lymphatic fluids.

### Efficiency of Biocides

Smith and Goodhue (31) reviewed the subject of the relation of particle size to efficiency of insecticides and concluded that toxicity tests show the smaller particles of solid insecticides to be, in general, the more effective. No such clear generalizations could be drawn for oil emulsions. Metcalf and Hess (32) found in airplane dusting of Paris green that the effectiveness was greatly reduced if the particle size was so small that the dust drifted away from the treatment area. Loss in toxicity was not evident in increasing from 10- to 20- up to 50-micron material, and a considerable improvement in the amount of dust reaching the desired area was achieved with the large particles.

Heuberger and Horsfall (33) report that the fungicidal and protective values of cuprous oxides vary inversely with the particle size.

### Uptake of Nutrients by Plants

The particle size of phosphate rock has been shown to be a significant variable in the yield and phosphorus uptake of alfalfa and buckwheat plants (34). Results on yields of alfalfa with varying treatments with

TABLE 1-2

Effect of Fineness of Grinding of Phosphate Rock on Yields of Alfalfa (34)

| Crop Number | Elapsed Time (days) | Yield in Grams[a] for | | | | |
|---|---|---|---|---|---|---|
| | | Control, No Phosphate Rock Added | Phosphate Rock Added | | | |
| | | | −100 +150 Mesh | −150 +325 Mesh | −100 Mesh | −325 Mesh |
| 1 | 61 | 34 | 65 | 68 | 75 | 78 |
| 2 | 24 | 35 | 50 | 54 | 56 | 59 |
| 3 | 22 | 38 | 55 | 58 | 60 | 62 |
| 4 | 32 | 35 | 42 | 44 | 48 | 49 |
| 5 | 72 | 29 | 72 | 75 | 82 | 86 |

[a] Each mesh size represents the accumulated averages of six sources of phosphate rock.

fractions of the same phosphate rock are reproduced in Table 1-2. Complete distribution data on the −100- and −325-mesh fractions could possibly explain the similarity of response of these two fractions. The fineness of the rock, however, was not as important as its source in determining its agronomic effectiveness.

## Setting Time of Cement

As pointed out earlier, chemical reactivity in general increases with decreasing particle size because of the greater surface available per unit weight in finer material. The decrease in the time required for concrete to set with increasing fineness of the particles has been cited as a good example of such an application of particle size information. Speed of construction and strength of the concrete are favored by fine material, but a compromise level is used to give adequate working time, a desirable rate of heat evolution, and a minimum of shrinking and cracking.

## Quality of Baked Goods

Particle size is one of the principal features discriminating flours that are suitable for cake making from those that will form a good bread dough (35). In addition, commercial flours must have a certain balance of protein and starch. Flours from different sources vary in their protein content, and the protein-to-starch ratio in a given flour varies with the size of the particle. Gracza (36) separated flour samples by air elutriation into two fractions of varying size distributions and correlated the composition of the fractions with the sharpness of separation between the distribution curves. Below a value of 32 microns, the finer fractions were richer in protein than the coarse fractions; whereas above this value the reverse was found. Thus, Gracza shows that it is possible to achieve a uniform level of protein through proper blending of the different size fractions.

## CHEMICAL AND PHYSICAL PROPERTIES AFFECTED BY PARTICLE SIZE

### Bulkiness and Packing

Bulkiness of a powder, defined as the reciprocal of the apparent density, $\rho(1 - \psi)$, where $\rho$ is true density and $\psi$ the void fraction, has been found to increase with decreasing particle size (37). Quantitative relationships are given by Roller (38) for anhydrite, gypsum, Portland cement, and chrome yellow powders. From the results shown in Fig. 1-3, the concept of a critical size, above which bulkiness is constant with size, was developed. The critical size ranges from 14 to 29 microns for these powders.

Measurement of bulk density under specified conditions has been described as an empirical means of determining average particle size (39). The bulk density will vary with the vibration to which the powder is subjected, and also with the uniformity of the particles, since voids in the structure of regular particles may be occupied by smaller particles. Furnas (40) has experimentally determined the voids in mix-

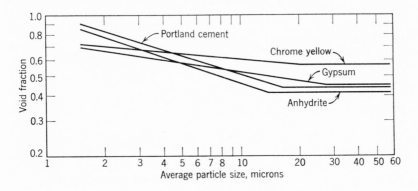

FIG. 1-3. Bulking properties of various powders.

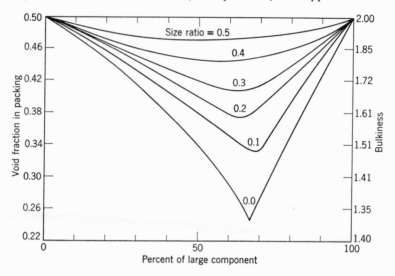

FIG. 1-4. Relation between voids and size composition in two-component systems of broken solids when the voids of single components are 0.5.

tures of two sized fractions and found that the voids went through a minimum for some intermediate mixture, as illustrated in Fig. 1-4. In addition, the voids were less the lower the size ratio between the fractions.

### Properties of Suspensions

A decrease in apparent fluidity of suspensions with decrease in particle size has been reported for zinc-oxide pigments in oil (41) and for glass spheres suspended in zinc bromide dissolved in aqueous glycerol (42). The apparent fluidity, however, of suspensions of glass spheres in a nonaqueous mixture of ethylene tetrabromide and diethylene glycol was found to be independent of particle diameter (42). Sweeney and Geckler qualitatively explain these apparently conflicting observations in the following way. Each particle is surrounded by an adsorbed layer of fluid which increases its effective size. The resulting increase in the volume concentration of particles is the largest for the small particles, and varies from fluid to fluid.

By using selected blends of particle sizes (glass spheres) of closely sized fractions, Sweeney and Geckler (42) were able to show that the fluidity of a suspension is dependent on the bulk density of the solids. This effect has been treated by other investigators (43).

The sedimentation of small particles suspended in liquids or gases is the basis for determining the size distribution of particulate matter and is also used to separate powdered material into various size fractions. Stokes' law is used to relate the rate of fall to the particle size. Although strictly applicable only to spherical particles, the relation holds very well for particles which differ appreciably from sphericity. Davies (44) has published an excellent article on the settling of suspended particles. The scattering of light by fine particles is responsible for natural phenomena such as the blue color of the sky, the brilliant colors of many sunsets, and the hazy appearance of the atmosphere. The theory of the scattering of light by fine particles was first developed by Rayleigh (45) and later extended by Mie (46).

### Flow of Powders

Flow experiments (47) with circular orifices have shown that, for each orifice, flow would not occur until a minimum particle size was exceeded. Beyond the minimum particle size, the rate of outflow first increased, then went through a maximum, and for the larger material decreased with increase in particle size. The size of the orifices used varied from $\frac{1}{32}$ to 1 in. and the finely divided materials were closely sized fractions of glass spheres in the range of 28–470 microns. The decrease in outflow with increase in particle size is in agreement with a study in the same size range by Bingham and Wikoff (48).

Franklin and Johanson (49) empirically related the mass flow rate from orifices of materials (in the range of 0.03 to 0.3 in.) with significant variables as follows:

$$W = \frac{\rho_B \times D_0^{2.93}}{(6.288\mu_3 + 23.16)(D_p + 1.889) - 44.90}$$

where $W$ is the mass rate of flow in pounds/minute, $\rho_B$ the density of material in pounds/cubic foot, $D_o$ the diameter of the orifice in inches, $D_p$ the diameter of the particle in inches, and $\mu_3$ the tangent of the internal kinetic angle of repose. In these studies, the bed height was greater than one column diameter, and the particle-to-orifice ratio and the orifice-to-column diameter exceeded certain minimum values. The columns used ranged from 1.8 to 8.8 in., the orifice diameters from 0.2 to 2.3 in., and the particle density from 7.3 to 676 lb/cu ft. Empirical correlations on the flow of sand (50) and catalyst pellets (51) have also been reported.

### Magnetic Properties

Selwood (52) has reviewed a number of investigations of the magnetic properties of finely divided materials in which the principal emphasis was on particle size. These include studies of graphite (53), the magnetic changes that occur in carbon during graphitization (54), quartz (55), and nickel in supported catalysts (56, 57). Bhatnager et al. (58) found that, in general, the magnetic susceptibility of powdered metals is independent of particle size. Problems of oxidation, contamination, or change of microcrystalline structure that may affect the susceptibility are difficult to avoid in finely divided metals.

## Solubility and Rate of Solution

The rate of dissolution of small particles is greater than that of large ones because the rate of dissolution of particulate matter is dependent on the specific surface in contact with the liquid medium (59).

Solubility has also been observed to be dependent on particle size. Several authors (60) have studied this phenomenon. Knapp (61), however, was the first to allow for any factor which would prevent the particles from attaining an indefinitely high value of supersolubility with extremely small size. He postulated the existence of an electrical charge on the particles and related the solubility of any given size particle, $S_r$, to the solubility of a very large particle, $S$, by the expression:

$$\frac{RT\mathrm{P}}{M} \ln \frac{S_r}{S} = \frac{2\sigma}{r} - \frac{q^2}{8\pi K} \cdot \frac{1}{r^4}$$

were $R$ is the gas constant, $T$ the absolute temperature, $\mathrm{P}$ the density of the bulk solid, $M$ the molecular weight, $r$ the radius of the particle,

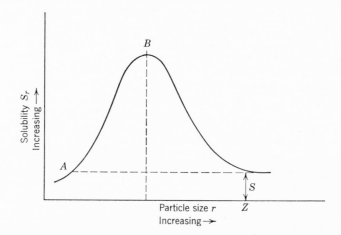

FIG. 1-5. Plot of Knapp's (61) expression for change in solubility with particle size. Reproduced from H. E. Buckley, *Crystal Growth*, John Wiley and Sons, 1951, p. 31.

**TABLE 1-3**

## Size Range of Typical Particles and Gas Dispersoids[a]

Particle diameter, microns

Equivalent sizes:

| (1 mμ) | | (1 cm) |
| --- | --- | --- |
| 0.001 | | 10,000 |

Angstrom units, Å

Tyler screen mesh: 400 250 150 | 35 20 10 | 6 4 | 3

U.S. screen mesh: 325 200 140 | 40 20 12 | 8 4 | 3

Theoretical mesh (Used very infrequently)

**Technical definitions**

Gas dispersoids —
Solid: Fume — Dust
Liquid: Mist — Spray

Soil: Clay — Silt — Fine sand — Coarse sand — Gravel
International std. classification system
Adopted by Internat. soc. soil sci. since 1934

**Common atmospheric dispersoids**

Smog
Clouds and fog — Mist — Drizzle — Rain

**Typical particles and gas dispersoids**

Rosin smoke
Oil smokes
Tobacco smoke
Metallurgical dusts and fumes
Ammonium chloride fume
Sulfuric
Concentrator mist
Sulfuric mist
Contact
Paint pigments
Zinc oxide fume
Insecticide dusts
Carbon black
Ground talc
Colloidal silica
Plant spores
Spray dried milk
Pollens
Alkali fume
Milled flour
Aitken nuclei
Atmospheric dust
Sea salt nuclei
Nebulizer drops
Combustion nuclei
Lung damaging dust
Pneumatic nozzle drops
Red blood cell diameter (adults): 7.5μ ± 0.3μ
Hydraulic nozzle drops
Bacteria
Human hair
Viruses

Fertilizer, ground limestone
Fly ash
Coal dust
Cement dust
Beach sand
Pulverized coal
Floration ores

Gas molecules
H₂  O₂  F₂  CO₂  Cl₂  C₆H₆
CO  H₂O  HCl  SO₂  C₄H₁₀
N₂  CH₄

Molecular diameters calculated from viscosity data at 0°C.

[a] Reproduced from reference 64, by permission from its author.

$\sigma$ the surface energy, $q$ the electric charge on the particle, and $K$ the dielectric constant of the substance. Graphical representation of this relation is shown in Fig. 1-5. The general observation is that the larger particles in a precipitate grow at the expense of the smaller ones below the size $R$. At the point $A$ in Fig. 1-5, where extremely small particles have a solubility corresponding to that of large crystals, such particles could theoretically remain in the presence of the large crystals (62).

### Size Range of Typical Particles

In the fall of 1961, the Stanford Research Institute published (63) in its Journal a series of articles under the heading "Fine Particle Research . . . Things Small, Effects Big." This series of articles illustrates the impact of fine particles on everyday life. The chart in one of these articles (64) shows the characteristics of particles and particle dispersoids. Portions of the chart showing the size of typical particles and gas dispersoids commonly encountered are reproduced in Table 1-3. Copies of the original chart are available free of charge from Department 300, Stanford Research Institute, Menlo Park, California.

**REFERENCES**

1. R. R. Irani, C. F. Callis, and T. Liu, *Ind. Eng. Chem.*, **51**, 1285 (1959).
2. B. S. Newman, in *Flow Properties of Disperse Systems,* J. J. Hermans, ed., Interscience Publishers, New York, 1953, p. 382.
3. J. Silverberg, J. R. Lehr, and G. Hoffmeister, *Agr. Chem.*, **12**, 38 (1957).
4. P. G. W. Hawksley, *Pulverized Coal Conference,* London, 1947, p. 679.
5. Reference 2, p. 412.
6. Technical bulletins TB-12, TB-36, Diamond Crystal Salt Co., St. Clair, Mich.
7. J .O. Hardesty and R. Kumagai, *Agr. Chem.*, **7** (2), 38 (1952).
8. ———, *ibid.*, **7** (3), 55 (1952).
9. R. Kumagai and J. O. Hardesty, *J. Agr. Food Chem.*, **4**, 132 (1956).
10. C. K. Lawrence, *Am. Fertilizer,* **102** (9), 7 (1945).
11. H. V. Moss, T. W. Schilb, and W. G. Warning, *Ind. Eng. Chem.*, **25**, 142 (1933).
12. J. Silverberg, J. R. Lehr, and G. Hoffmeister, *Agr. Chem.*, **12**, 38 (1957).
13. A. L. Whynes and T. P. Dee, *J. Sci. Food Agr.*, **8**, 577 (1957).
14. C. G. Harmen and F. Fraulini, *J. Am. Ceram. Soc.*, **19**, 252 (1940).
15. J. M. Dallavalle, *Micromeritics,* Pitman Publishing Corp., New York, second edition, 1948, p. 256.
16. D. J. Price and H. H. Brown, *Dust Explosions,* National Fire Protection Assoc., Boston, 1922.
17. R. V. Wheeler, *Trans. Faraday Soc.*, **32**, 1244 (1936).
18. C. E. Barnett, *Ind. Eng. Chem.*, **41**, 272 (1949).
19. W. G. Wade, *J. Oil Colour Chemists' Assoc.*, **42**, 548 (1959).
20. R. D. Cadle, *Particle Size Determination,* Interscience Publishers, New York, 1955, p. 13.

21. H. W. Siesholts and L. H. Cohan, *Ind. Eng. Chem.,* **41,** 390 (1949).

22. A. C. C. Newman, *Symposium on Particle Size Analysis,* p. 69, supplement to *Trans. Inst. Chem. Engrs. (London),* **25** (1947).

23. S. D. Gershon, H. H. Pokras, and T. H. Rider, in E. Sagarin, ed., *Cosmetics: Science and Technology,* Interscience Publishers, New York, 1957, p. 316.

24. M. L. Smith, *J. Soc. Chem. Ind. (London),* **54,** 269 (1935).

25. S. Epstein and M. L. Tainter, *J. Dental Res.,* **22,** 335 (1943).

26. S. Rubin, *J. Atmospheric Terrest. Phys.,* **2** (2), 130 (1952).

27. Reference 20, p. 15.

28. L. Dautrebande, R. Perthel, R. Copps, and J. Shaver, *Arch. Intern. Pharmacodyn.* **84,** 1 (1950).

29. A. H. M. Andreasen, N. Hofmanbang, and N. H. Rasmussen, *Kolloid-Z.,* **86,** 70 (1939).

30. H. E. Rose, *The Measurement of Particle Size in Very Fine Powders,* Chemical Publishing Co., New York, 1954, p. 20.

31. C. M. Smith and L. D. Goodhue, *Ind. Eng. Chem.,* **34,** 490 (1942).

32. R. L. Metcalf and A. D. Hess, *Public Health Rept. (U. S.),* **59,** 1458 (1944).

33. J. W. Heuberger and J. G. Horsfall, *Phytopathology,* **29,** 303 (1939).

34. W. H. Armiger and M. Fried, *J. Agr. Food Chem.,* **6,** 539 (1958).

35. E. G. Richardson, *Nature,* **148,** 715 (1941).

36. R. Gracza, *Cereal Chem.,* **36,** 465 (1959).

37. Reference 15, pp. 143–144.

38. P. S. Roller, *Ind. Eng. Chem.,* **22,** 1206 (1930).

39. F. S. Sinnat and L. Slater, *Fuel,* **2,** 142 (1932).

40. C. C. Furnas, *Ind. Eng. Chem.,* **23,** 1052 (1932).

41. R. N. Weltmann and H. Green, *J. Appl. Phys.,* **14,** 569 (1943).

42. K. H. Sweeny and R .D. Geckler, *ibid.,* **25,** 1135 (1954).

43. R. Roscoe, *Brit. J. Appl. Phys.,* **3,** 267 (1952); M. Mooney, *J. Colloid Sci.,* **6,** 162 (1951); S. H. Maron, B. D. Madow, and I. M. Krieger, *J. Colloid Sci.,* **6,** 584 (1951).

44. C. N. Davies, *Symposium on Particle Size Analysis,* p. 25, Supplement to *Trans. Inst. Chem. Engrs. (London),* **25,** 1947.

45. Lord Rayleigh, *Scientific Papers,* Cambridge University Press, London, 1899, Vol. I, p. 92.

46. G. Mie, *Ann. Physik,* **25,** 377 (1908).

47. R. R. Irani, unpublished data, Monsanto Chemical Co., St. Louis, Mo.

48. E. C. Bingham and R. W. Wikoff, *J. Rheol.,* **2,** 395 (1931).

49. F. C. Franklin and L. N. Johanson, *Chem. Eng. Sci.,* **4,** 119 (1955).

50. E. C. Bingham and R. W. Wikoff, *J. Rheol.,* **2,** 395 (1931).

51. R. H. Newton, G. S. Dunham, and T. P. Simpson, *Trans. Am. Inst. Chem. Engrs.,* **41,** 219 (1945).

52. P. W. Selwood, *Magnetochemistry,* Interscience Publishers, New York, 1956, second edition, pp. 91, 123–125, 352, 389.

53. R. Rao, *Indian J. Phys.,* **6,** 241 (1931).

54. W. F. Wynne-Jones, H. E. Blayden, and R. Iley, *Brenstoff-Chem.,* **33,** 268 (1952); H. Houda, K. Ouchi, and K. Nagata, *J. Chem. Soc. (Japan),* **74,** 720 (1953); H. T. Pinnick, *Phys. Rev.,* **94,** 319 (1954).

55. Y. Shimizu and N. Takatori, *Sci. Rept. Tohoku Univ., K. Honda Anniversary Vol., First Ser.,* 306 (1936).

56. A. Michel, *Ann. Chem.*, **8**, 317 (1937); A. Michel and M. Gallissot, *Compt. Rend.*, **206**, 1252 (1938); A. Michel, R. Bermer, and G. LeClerc, *J. Chem. Phys.*, **47**, 269 (1950).

57. P. W. Selwood, S. Adler, and T. R. Phillips, *J. Am. Chem. Soc.*, **76**, 2281 (1954); *ibid.*, **77**, 1462 (1955).

58. S. S. Bhatnagar, M. R. Verma, and M. Anwarul-Haq, *Kolloid-Z.*, **78**, 9 (1937).

59. T. H. James and W. Vansdow, *J. Phys. Chem.*, **62**, 1189 (1958); T. L. O'Connor and S. A. Greenberg, *ibid.*, **62**, 1195 (1959).

60. For example, see Wilh. Ostwald, *Z. Physik. Chem.*, **34**, 493 (1900); M. Jones and J. R. Partington, *J. Chem. Soc.*, **107**, 1019 (1915); M. L. Dundon and E. Mack, *J. Am. Chem. Soc.*, **45**, 2479 (1923); R. Gross, *Jahrb. Radioakt. u. Elektronik*, **15**, 270 (1918).

61. L. F. Knapp, *Trans. Faraday Soc.*, **17**, 457 (1922).

62. H. E. Buckley, *Crystal Growth*, John Wiley and Sons, New York, 1951, p. 31.

63. *J. Stanford Res. Inst.*, **5**, 95–132 (1961).

64. C. E. Lapple, *ibid.*, **5**, 95 (1961)

*chapter 2*

# Definitions

Before attempting any detailed discussion of particle size measurements, data presentation, or data interpretation, we shall establish a set of consistent yet concise definitions regarding significant terms unique to the specification of the state of subdivision of matter. All these definitions conform with accepted ASTM terminology (1).

### Particle (Working Unit)

The individual physical unit describing the state of subdivision of matter is referred to as a particle. The particle is a common working unit used to describe particulate matter. On examination of various particles, however, wide size variations are observed. Thus it is necessary to clarify the definition so that each individual particulate unit encountered can be discussed in terms of the cohesive forces involved.

We define a particle of a substance as that state of subdivision of matter whose shape depends on the process by which it was formed and on the intramolecular cohesive forces present. Such a definition describes equally well all particulate entities. Thus, a particle may be a single crystal, a liquid droplet, or an amorphous material.

### Aggregate

An aggregate is a particle or an assembly of particles held together by strong inter- or intramolecular or atomic cohesive forces. It is stable to normal handling and ordinary dispersive techniques such as high-speed mixing and ultrasonics.

*17*

The dimensions of a solid aggregate are controlled by crystal growth, fusion, or smaller-particle coalescence. Aggregate dimensions are normally decreased by grinding and are increased by fusion. Solid aggregates can be dimensionally increased by first wetting the surface with a solvent in which the material is soluble and then evaporating the solvent. This process yields a bridging network between the smaller particles through a homogeneous surface solution.

The dimensions of fluid aggregate can be decreased by emulsification or increased by flocculation. The cohesive forces responsible for aggregate formation in fluids are usually weaker than those present in crystalline solids; however, they may approach those responsible for the cohesion of amorphous solid aggregates.

### Agglomerate

An agglomerate is composed of two or more particles and/or aggregates held together by relatively weak cohesive forces. In many samples encountered, these forces are due to an electrostatic surface charge (2) generated during a handling or processing operation.

The smaller the particle dimensions, the greater the specific surface charge density, hence the more severe the agglomeration. For extremely finely divided particles (about 0.1 micron), the cohesive forces responsible for agglomeration approach as a limit in many cases the strength of the cohesive forces present in amorphous solid aggregates.

Agglomerates can be broken by dispersion methods such as fluidization or deflocculation. It is important to note that, although an aggregate may describe the working unit, an agglomerate does not describe any working unit. Thus, sample deagglomeration techniques are extremely important in any measurement method. A thorough discussion of agglomerate dispersion is presented in Chapters 5 and 6.

### Ultimate Particle

It is apparent from the preceding discussion that a unit of subdivision smaller than an aggregate may occur. Let us define an ultimate particle of a substance as the smallest state of subdivision which retains all the physical and chemical properties of that substance. For a crystalline substance, the ultimate particle is normally an assembly of unit cells. Although no ordered structure occurs in a completely amorphous substance, the ultimate particle represents the smallest group of molecules which satisfies our definition. Furthermore, the size of the ultimate particle of a fluid may approach the dimensions of a single molecule. Thus the aggregate, the normally encountered working unit of subdivision, is a group of ultimate particles bonded by strong cohesive forces, whereas by comparison an agglomerate represents two or more particles and/or aggregates held together by weak cohesive forces.

## Size

The size of a particle is the representative dimension that best describes the degree of comminution of the particle. For a spherically symmetric particle the diameter is that dimension and thus is its size. The diameter $d_j$ of a particle deviating from spherical symmetry may be defined as any one dimensional distance between two points on the external surface of the particle that intersects the center of gravity of the particle. A large number (approaching infinity) of nonequivalent diameters satisfying this definition are possible for an irregular particle. The distribution of these diameters is continuous between an upper and a lower limit. Therefore, the size of any irregular particle is a statistical average of all these nonequivalent diameters. Consequently, the size of a given particle depends on the averaging method.

For any given irregular particle, a maximum diameter $d_m$ and a minimum diameter $d_s$ can be located. The value of any other diameter satisfying our definition lies between $d_m$ and $d_s$. Some averaging methods used to obtain a meaningful statistical representative size of an irregular particle are given in Table 2-1.

TABLE 2-1

Averaging Methods

| Size Representation | | Method of Averaging |
|---|---|---|
| Geometric mean of diameters* | $M_1$ | $\left( \prod_{d_i=d_s}^{d_m} d_i \right)^{1/n}$ <br> where $n$ is the number of diameters used |
| Arithmetic mean of diameters | $M_2$ | $\frac{1}{n} \sum_{d_i=d_s}^{d_m} d_i$ |
| Harmonic mean of diameters | $M_3$ | $\left( \frac{1}{n} \sum_{d_i=d_s}^{d_m} \frac{1}{d_i} \right)^{-1}$ |

* $\pi$ means the product of all of the $d_i$ terms.

With any particle size measurement there coexists an inherent diameter average. For example, provided no preferred orientation is encountered, the size obtained from microscopic area measurements is the geometric average of the diameters, $M_1$. Unidirectional microscopic length measurements directly give the arithmetic average of the diameters, $M_2$. When the size is obtained from settling velocities, the opposing force to sedimentation is proportional to $M_1$.

The numerical values of the commonly employed particle sizes lie between the arithmetic average and the geometric average of the nonequivalent diameters. Table 2-2 demonstrates that the geometric average and the arithmetic average approach one another as the number of measured (averaged) diameters is increased (3).

TABLE 2-2

| Ratio of Maximum to Minimum Diameter | Number of Measured (Averaged) Diameters | % Deviation between Sizes from Geometric and Arithmetic Averages[a,b] |
|:---:|:---:|:---:|
| 2 | 2 | 6 |
|  | 4 | 3 |
|  | 6 | 3 |
|  | 10 | 2 |
|  | 100 | 2 |
| 3 | 2 | 13 |
|  | 4 | 8 |
|  | 6 | 6 |
|  | 10 | 5 |
|  | 100 | 4 |
| 4 | 2 | 20 |
|  | 4 | 12 |
|  | 6 | 10 |
|  | 10 | 8 |
|  | 100 | 6 |
| 10 | 2 | 43 |
|  | 4 | 27 |
|  | 6 | 22 |
|  | 10 | 18 |
|  | 100 | 11 |

[a] Assuming equal diameter intervals.

[b] $100 \left( 1 - \dfrac{M_1}{M_2} \right)$.

## Particle Shape

Since the normally encountered solid particle is usually not spherically symmetric, a description of particle shape may be useful. Wide variations in particle shape are evident in solids. Because of lack of rigidity, however, the particle shapes exhibited by droplets do not show such radical shapes as those found in solids. Various shape factors have been described in order to report the type of shape measured. The ratio of the measured maximum diameter to the measured minimum diameter may be used to represent shape. As indicated in Table 2-2 this shape factor is relatively unimportant for ratios less than 4. As many particles have a maximum-diameter ratio of 4 or less, shape factors are not generally reported. When diameter ratios greater than 4 are encountered, however, discrepancies in size measurements by methods employing the same type of statistical averaging will occur. Therefore, a shape factor may be considered as that factor required to make the statistical averaging independent of the measurement (4).

It is apparent that such a shape factor need not be $d_m/d_s$. Further discussion of this type of shape factor will be given when different measurement methods are compared.

Green (5) and Perrot and Kinney (6) defined a shape factor as the ratio between the actual surface or volume of the particles and that obtained from size measurement. Since various particle sizes are determined by size measurement methods, whereas a total surface or volume is obtained from experimental measurements, these shape factors may also be regarded as proportionality factors between integrated differential methods and integral methods.

The term sphericity has been defined by Wadell (7) as the ratio of the external surface area of a sphere to that of a particle of equivalent volume. This ratio is really a shape factor which represents the deviation of a particle from spherical symmetry. It may be required when the sizes of irregular particles are treated as equivalent spheres.

## Particle Size Distributions

A monodisperse system of particles is composed of the same-sized particles, whereas different-sized particles are found in a polydisperse particle system. The occurrence of monodisperse particle systems is rare; polydisperse particle systems are commonly encountered.

In size measurements on polydisperse particle systems, the probability that a given particle picked at random has a specified size is measured. Thus the particle sizes reported for any material are associated with their frequency of occurrence. The frequency of occurrence may be reported as the number of particles or as a weight greater than or smaller than a stated size or range of sizes. When the frequency of occurrence of particle sizes is determined by a number, a number-size distribution is obtained; weight-size distributions are obtained when

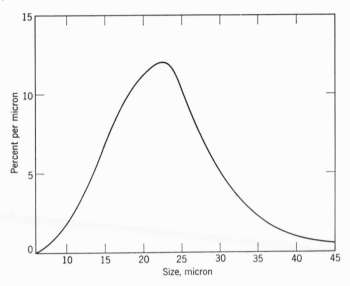

FIG. 2-1. Size frequency of a number-size distribution.

size frequencies are measured on a weight basis. Number-size distributions are normally obtained from microscopic size measurements; size frequency measurements made by sieving represent weight-size distributions. Further discussion of other size frequency functions used in reporting particle size measurements is given in Chapter 4.

When the size measurement data are divided into groups of equal size range, each group will include a certain percentage of the size measurements. A differential size frequency curve is obtained when this percentage is plotted against the mean of the size range. Figure 2-1 is a size frequency plot of a number-size distribution. This size frequency curve has one peak, and the number-size distribution which it represents is a homogeneous (unimodal) distribution; that is, the distribution has one mean size.

Size distributions having two or more mean sizes are described as heterogeneous (multimodal) distributions; such a distribution is usually a mixture of two or more homogeneous (unimodal) distributions.

The number and/or weight size distribution data for many particulates follow well-known probability statistics. Hatch and Choate (8) among others (9) (see also Chapter 4), have shown that many number- and/or weight-size distributions follow the logarithmic form of the Gaussian statistical law of errors (normal law). Thus the two well-established parameters of the log-normal law, often evaluated graphically, adequately describe size distributions of particulate matter. It is important to note that when the log-normal law is employed the statistical mean and the deviation from the mean are changed from arithmetic to geometric averaging. The geometric standard deviation is a unitless ratio, as will be shown in Chapter 4, whereas the arithmetic standard deviation has the same units as the arithmetic mean.

If $P(M)$ represents the frequency of occurrence per size unit for a number or weight size distribution, then

$$100 \frac{P(M)}{\int_0^\infty P(M)\,dM}$$

is by definition the size frequency expressed as a percent by number or weight.

The total percent by number or weight smaller than a given size or size range is the cumulative undersize. Thus the cumulative undersize for size $M_1$ is given by

$$100 \frac{\int_0^{M_1} P(M)\,dM}{\int_0^\infty P(M)\,dM}$$

The cumulative oversize is the total percent by weight or number larger than a given size or size range. Based on the equation for the cumulative undersize, the cumulative oversize is simply

$$100 - 100 \left[ \frac{\int_0^{M_1} P(M)\,dM}{\int_0^\infty P(M)\,dM} \right]$$

or

$$100 \left\{ \frac{\int_{M_1}^\infty [P(M)\,dM]}{\int_0^\infty P(M)\,dM} \right\}$$

**Average Particle Size**

The average particle size should be chosen so that it is the best single value that represents the whole size distribution for the purpose involved. Many times no such single number can describe the whole particle size distribution adequately, and other parameters must be specified. When an average particle size is given, however, it is extremely important to specify what sort of average it represents.

**Nonuniformity (Dispersion)**

Nonuniformity is a measure of the spread in particle sizes around the average or mean size. In statistics this is termed dispersion. If the geometric mean is used as the average size, the dispersion is usually expressed as the geometric standard deviation.

**REFERENCES**

1. ASTM, Designation E20-51T (1951).
2. References cited by R. R. Irani, C. F. Callis, and T. Liu, *Ind. Eng. Chem.*, **51**, 1285 (1959).
3. R. R. Irani and D. P. Ames, *Mater. Res. Std.*, **1**, 637, (1961).
4. G. Herdan, *Small Particle Statistics*, Elsevier, Houston, 1953, p. 230.
5. H. L. Green, *J. Franklin Inst.* **204**, 713 (1927).
6. G. J. Perrot and S. P. Kinney, *J. Am. Ceram. Soc.* **6**, 417 (1923).
7. H. Wadell, *J. Geol.*, **4**, 310 (1932). *J. Franklin Inst.*, **217**, 459 (1934).
8. T. Hatch and S. P. Choate, *J. Franklin Inst.*, **207**, 369 (1929).
9. D. P. Ames, R. R. Irani, and C. F. Callis, *J. Phys. Chem.*, **61**, 531 (1959).

*chapter 3*

# Methods of data presentation

Generally speaking, the purpose of a particle size measurement is to discover the true frequency distribution of particle size. The observed distribution serves as the basic data from which may be derived certain representative constants, for example, the median size; or modified relative frequency distributions obtained by transformation, for example, percent by weight from percent by number. With the realization of the role played by particle size in scientific and industrial fields, the need for adequate presentation of the data becomes apparent.

In 1933 Dunn and Shaw (1) presented a discussion of the factors involved in the presentation and comparison of particle size data. They assumed microscopic examination, however, to be the basis of all measurements. In the following paragraphs we make a more general presentation.

The most precise and general method of data presentation is the tabular form, since the data can be expressed explicitly. The table can be a listing of size versus one of the many ways of expressing their distribution, for example, size frequency or size cumulation. As was discussed in Chapter 2 and will be shown in Fig. 3-4, when size distributions are reported, it is essential to specify which weighting process is employed, since, for example, number-size and weight-size distributions are in general radically different. The problem of weighting is covered in more detail in Chapter 4. If it is unknown what the

TABLE 3-1

Size Distribution of a Sample of Glass Beads

| | Cumulative Distribution | | | |
| | Weight Distribution | | Number Distribution | |
| Size (microns) | % Cumulative (Greater than) | % Finer than | % Cumulative (Greater than) | % Finer than |
|---|---|---|---|---|
| 5 | 100.0 | 0.0 | 100.0 | 0.0 |
| 10 | 99.9 | 0.1 | 99.0 | 1.0 |
| 15 | 98.4 | 1.6 | 86.2 | 13.8 |
| 20 | 89.5 | 10.5 | 58.0 | 42.0 |
| 25 | 71.5 | 28.5 | 32.0 | 68.0 |
| 30 | 50.0 | 50.0 | 15.0 | 85.0 |
| 35 | 32.1 | 67.9 | 7.0 | 93.0 |
| 40 | 19.2 | 80.8 | 2.8 | 97.2 |
| 45 | 10.8 | 89.2 | 1.2 | 98.8 |
| 50 | 6.0 | 94.0 | 0.5 | 99.5 |
| 55 | 3.0 | 97.0 | 0.15 | 99.85 |
| 60 | 1.9 | 98.1 | 0.09 | 99.91 |
| 100 | 0.0 | 100.0 | 0.0 | 100.0 |

| | Frequency Distribution | |
| Size Range | Weight Distribution: Percent Frequency | Number Distribution: Percent Frequency |
|---|---|---|
| 0–5 | 0.0 | 0.0 |
| 5–10 | 0.1 | 1.0 |
| 10–15 | 1.5 | 12.8 |
| 15–20 | 8.9 | 28.2 |
| 20–25 | 18.0 | 26.0 |
| 25–30 | 21.5 | 17.0 |
| 30–35 | 17.9 | 8.0 |
| 35–40 | 12.9 | 4.2 |
| 40–45 | 10.4 | 1.6 |
| 45–50 | 2.8 | 0.7 |
| 50–55 | 3.0 | 0.35 |
| 55–60 | 1.1 | 0.06 |
| 60–100 | 1.9 | 0.09 |
| 0–100—Total | 100.0 | 100.00 |

distribution units represent, as is the case with some of the empirical methods, the technique of measurement should be specified.

Table 3-1 is a tabulation of the size distribution of a sample of spherical glass beads expressed both on a weight-size and on a number-size basis. The distributions are presented both as frequencies and as cumulative frequencies. The terms frequency and cumulative have been defined in Chapter 2.

In spite of the foregoing, there are several important reasons for presenting particle size distributions graphically. One reason is that graphs present data in such a form that approximate values of the deviation and skewness of the data from the mean and the location of the mean can be visually obtained. Graphs are also more concise than long tables of measurements in their original form. In some cases, graphs yield specific numerical values or constants which describe the size distribution, for example, the mean and the median. Naturally, if the size distribution closely follows a certain mathematical function, then the parameters of such a distribution law suffice to define the complete distribution curve.

Since, as was discussed in Chapter 1, most size distribution analyses are performed in order to control or study another property of the powder, many comparisons are usually made between samples. When a large number of samples have to be compared, or certain correlations with other variables are being investigated, the graphical and the mathematical presentations become much more desirable than tabular forms.

Summarized next are the different ways of presenting size distributions graphically, with the errors shown in the figures being ±1%.

## Histograms

A histogram is a plot of the frequency of occurrence as a function of the size range. The histogram shown in Fig. 3-1 is for a powder that is said to be log-normally distributed, whereas Fig. 3-5 is for a powder that deviates from log-normality. Many types of histograms can be constructed. For example, Figs. 3-2 and 3-6 are plots of the frequency of occurrence against the logarithm of the size range for the powders corresponding to Figs. 3-1 and 3-5 respectively. The ordinate of the histograms, the frequency, can represent number, weight, surface area, or any other weighting process, in the specific size interval.

## Size Frequency Curves

Size frequency curves can be best thought of as smoothed-out histograms. These curves are justifiable only when a large number of points are utilized. The smooth curves in Figs. 3-2 and 3-6 are size frequency

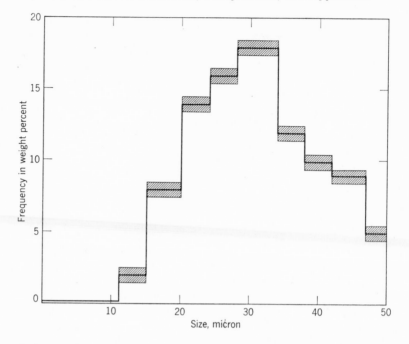

FIG. 3-1. Histogram plot for a simple log-normal distribution (size on linear scale).

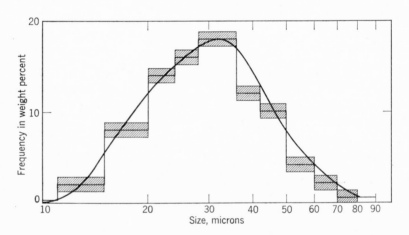

FIG. 3-2. Histogram and size-frequency plots for a simple log-normal distribution (size on logarithmic scale).

curves of the indicated histograms. It is obvious that for log-normal distributions symmetric plots are obtained when the log of the size is plotted against frequency of occurrence.

In general, the area under size frequency plots is finite, and if by normalization it is set equal to unity, the area between any interval on the abscissa and the curve above that interval is equal to the probability that a particle chosen at random from the population will have a particle size within that interval.

## Cumulative Plots

Cumulative plots can be described as those which involve plotting the percent of particles greater than (or less than) a given particle size against the particle size. Thus the limiting values of the ordinate vary from 0 to 100%. The ordinate can represent total surface, external surface, weight, number of particles, or any other basis. Figure 3-3 is

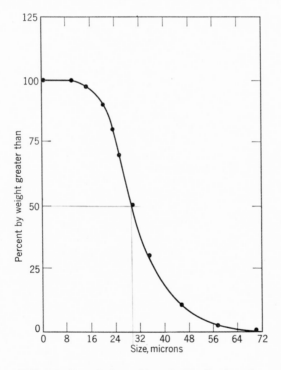

FIG. 3-3. Cumulative arithmetic distribution plot for a simple log-normal distribution.

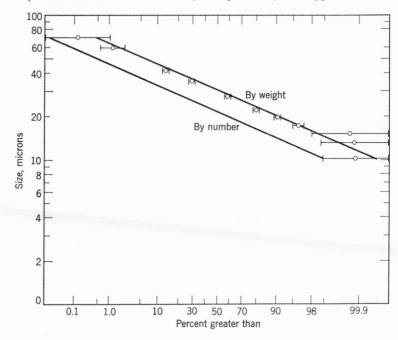

FIG. 3-4. Log-probability plot for a simple log-normal distribution.

a cumulative plot of the weight-size distribution of the same sample shown in Figs. 3-1 and 3-2. Figure 3-7 is the plot corresponding to Figs. 3-5 and 3-6. From examining Figs. 3-3 and 3-7, it is obvious that this method of plotting does not differentiate between log-normal and other distributions.

## The Use of Probability Paper

Cumulative plots such as shown in Figs. 3-3 and 3-7 are used extensively, but their interpretation and comparison can be considerably enhanced by using the generally applicable log-normal distribution plot or one of its modifications (2). Figure 3-4 is a plot on log probability paper (for example, Keuffel and Esser No. 359–24), first proposed by Hatch (3), of the size distribution for a material that is said to have a log-normal distribution. Figure 3-8 is a similar plot for the same powder shown in Figs. 3-5, 3-6, and 3-7.

The data in Fig. 3-8 are not distributed log-normally, and they follow one of the modifications to be covered in Chapter 4. In some

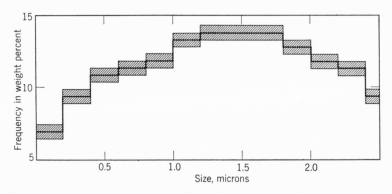

FIG. 3-5. Histogram plot for a modified log-normal distribution (size on linear scale).

cases, the particle size distribution plot on log probability paper may superficially appear not to be log-normally distributed because of the following reasons.

If the abscissa units are examined in Figs. 3-4 and 3-8, we note that for a given abscissa distance a 1% unit around 95% probability is about four times as great as that around 50% probability, and that the same holds true for the corresponding units at the low probabilities. Therefore, the units are increasingly exaggerated as we recede in both

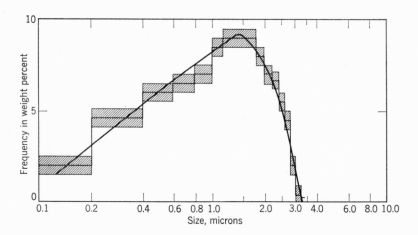

FIG. 3-6. Histogram plot for a modified log-normal distribution (size on logarithmic scale).

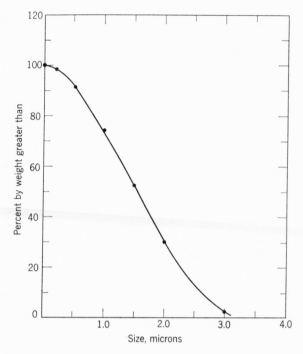

FIG. 3-7. Cumulative arithmetic distribution plot for a
modified log-normal distribution.

directions from the 50% probability locations, and naturally the deviations from a straight line are exaggerated on both ends of the distribution. In addition, most particle size distribution measurements, as is
discussed in Chapters 5–9, suffer from inaccuracies at both ends of the
distribution, tending to exaggerate the deviations further. Thus, although a powder might be truly log-normally distributed, one or both
ends of the distributions might appear curved because of artificial
enlargement of the deviations. Kottler (4–6) recognized these difficulties and proposed an algebraic weighted evaluation of the data that is
reminiscent of the chi square summation. Kottler's algebraic evaluation
is time consuming (about 1 hour per distribution) and can be only
justified in the most accurate work, since with experience the ends of
the distribution curve can be visually underweighted as compared with
the points around 50% probability.

If the upper and/or the lower ends of the particle size distribution
are either limited or removed, and/or mixtures of powders are encountered, truly nonlinear plots are found on logarithm probability

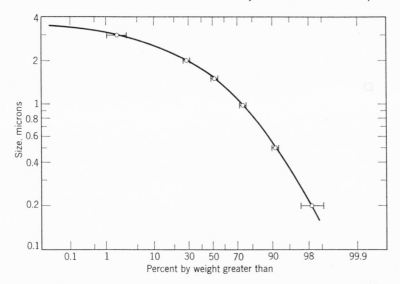

FIG. 3-8. Log probability plot for a modified log-normal distribution.

paper, as illustrated in Fig. 3-8. The interpretation of these deviations has been discussed by Irani (2) and is more fully evaluated in Chapter 4.

**REFERENCES**

1. E. J. Dunn and J. Shaw, *Proc. ASTM*, **33**, Part II, 692 (1933).
2. R. R. Irani, *J. Phys. Chem.*, **63**, 1603 (1959).
3. T. Hatch and S. P. Choate, *J. Franklin Inst.*, **207**, 369 (1929).
4. F. Kottler, *J. Franklin Inst.*, **250**, 419 (1950).
5. ———, *ibid.*, **251**, 499 (1951).
6. ———, *ibid.*, **251**, 617 (1951).

*chapter 4*

# Distribution functions applicable
# to particle size distributions

Because particulate matter is predominantly found to be a distribution of particle sizes, the distribution functions relevant to particle size distributions are developed in this chapter. Prior, however, to considering the distribution laws that pertain to particle sizing in general, some more fundamental distribution laws will be considered in order to help with the understanding of the basic significance of particle size distributions.

## BINOMIAL DISTRIBUTION LAW

### Theorem

Given a very large set of objects in which the probability of finding an object of a particular kind $w$ is $p$, then if $n$ objects are withdrawn from the set, the probability that exactly $r$ of the $n$ objects are of the kind $w$ is given by

$$\frac{n!p^r(1-p)^{(n-r)}}{(n-r)!r!}$$

This is called the binomial distribution law because $n!/(n-r)!r!$ (sometimes called $_nC_r$) is the coefficient of $x^r$ in the binomial expansion of $(1+x)^n$.

To prove this theorem, consider first a particular set containing $r$ of the $n$ objects. The probability that the first of these $r$ objects has the property $w$ is $p$, the probability that the first and second have the

*34*

property $w$ is $p^2$. Similarly, the probability that the first of the remaining $r$ objects does not have the property $w$ is $1 - p$, and the probability that none of these $n - r$ objects have the property $w$ is $(1 - p)^{(n-r)}$. Therefore, the probability that just the $r$ specified objects have the property $w$ is $p^r(1 - p)^{(n-r)}$. Instead of the probability of all the members of a specified set of $r$ objects having the property $w$, however, we wish to find the probability of some set of $r$ objects having the property $w$. We must therefore multiply the given probability by the number of ways in which a set of $r$ objects can be selected from the total set of $n$ objects.

The first member of the set can clearly be selected in $n$ different ways, the second member in $n - 1$ ways, the $r$th member in $n - r + 1$ ways. So the total number of ways in which the set of $r$ objects can be selected is

$$n(n - 1) \cdots (n - r + 1) = \frac{n!}{(n - r)!} \qquad (1)$$

We have counted, however, all the ways in which the order as well as the identity of the $r$ objects differed. Therefore, we have to divide by the number of permutations of $r$ objects, which is $r!$. Thus the total number of sets containing $r$ of the $n$ objects is $n!/(n - r)!r!$ and the probability that exactly $r$ or the $n$ objects have the property $w$ is

$$\frac{n!}{(n - r)!r!} p^r(1 - p)^{(n-r)} \qquad (2)$$

or

$$p_w{}^r = {}_nC_r \, p^r q^{(n-r)} \qquad (3)$$

where

$$q = (1 - p) \qquad (4)$$

## Average Value for a Set of Numbers Obeying the Binomial Distribution Law

The average value of a property of $r$ is

$$\bar{r} = \sum_{r=0}^{r=n} r \cdot (p_w{}^r) = \sum_{r=0}^{r=n} r \cdot ({}_nC_r)(p^r)(q^{(n-r)}) \qquad (5)$$

To obtain an explicit expression for $r$, consider the binomial expansion of $(p + q)^n$, which is

$$(p + q)^n = \sum_{r=0}^{r=n} ({}_nC_r)(p^r)(q^{(n-r)}) = \sum_{r=0}^{r=n} p_w{}^r \qquad (6)$$

Also introduce an auxiliary variable $X$. Equation 6 becomes

$$(pX + q)^n = \sum_{r=0}^{r=n} ({}_nC_r)(p^r)(X^r)(q^{(n-r)}) = \sum_{r=0}^{r=n} (X^r)(p_w{}^r) \qquad (7)$$

Differentiation of equation 7 with respect to $X$ gives

$$np(pX + q)^{(n-1)} = \sum_{r=0}^{r=n} r(X^{(r-1)})(p_w{}^r) \tag{8}$$

If $X = 1$, and using equation 4:

$$np = \sum_{r=0}^{r=n} r(p_w{}^r) \tag{9}$$

or according to equation 5

$$\bar{r} = np \tag{10}$$

## The Standard Deviation for a Set of Numbers Obeying the Binomial Distribution Law

The standard deviation $\sigma_r$ for $r$ objects can be defined as

$$\sigma_r{}^2 = \frac{1}{n} \sum_{i=1}^{i=n} (r_i - \bar{r})^2 \tag{11}$$

or

$$\sigma_r{}^2 = \frac{1}{n} \sum_{i=1}^{i=n} r_i{}^2 - \frac{2}{n} \sum_{i=1}^{i=n} r_i\bar{r} + \frac{1}{n} \sum_{i=1}^{i=n} \bar{r}^2$$

$$= \overline{r^2} - 2\bar{r}^2 + \bar{r}^2 \tag{12}$$

Therefore

$$\sigma_r{}^2 = \overline{r^2} - \bar{r}^2 \tag{13}$$

To evaluate $\sigma_r$ in terms of $p$, $q$, and $r$, differentiate equation 8 once more with respect to $X$:

$$n(n-1)p^2 (pX + q)^{(n-2)} = \sum_{r=0}^{r=n} r^2 (p_w{}^r)(X^{(r-2)}) - \sum_{r=0}^{r=n} r \, p_w{}^r \, X^{(r-2)} \tag{14}$$

Again let $X = 1$ and use equations 4 and 6:

$$n(n-1) p^2 = \overline{r^2} - \bar{r} \tag{15}$$

Combining equations 13 and 15:

$$\sigma_r{}^2 = n(n-1) p^2 + \bar{r} - \bar{r}^2 \tag{16}$$

Substituting the value of $\bar{r}$ from equation 10 yields:

$$\sigma_r = \sqrt{npq} \tag{17}$$

### THE GAUSSIAN (NORMAL) DISTRIBUTION LAW

For large values of $n$ (meaning in the case of particle size a large number of particles considered), the binomial distribution law is difficult to evaluate and does not give a concise idea of how the probabilities change with the value of the variable. For large values of $n$, the Gaussian law can be derived from the binomial distribution law as follows.

Let $x$ be the deviation of a certain object from the average value $r$, $(np)$:

$$r = np + x \qquad (18)$$

Then equation 3 becomes

$$p_w{}^r = {}_nC_{(np+x)}p^{(np+x)}q^{[n-(np+x)]} \qquad (19)$$

$$p_w^{(np+x)} = \frac{n!}{(nq-x)!\,(np+x)!}\,p^{(np+x)}q^{[n-(np+x)]} \qquad (20)$$

For large values of $n$, and as a result of evaluation of appropriate gamma functions, Stirling showed that

$$\ln (Z!) = Z \ln Z - Z + \tfrac{1}{2} \ln (2\pi Z) \qquad (21)$$

Thus equation 20 can be written in the form

$$\ln p_w{}^r = n \ln n - n + \tfrac{1}{2} \ln 2\pi n - (nq - x) \ln \left[ nq \left( 1 - \frac{x}{nq} \right) \right]$$

$$+ (nq - x) - \tfrac{1}{2} \ln \left[ 2\pi nq \left( 1 - \frac{x}{nq} \right) \right]$$

$$- (np + x) \ln \left[ np \left( 1 + \frac{x}{np} \right) \right]$$

$$+ (np + x) - \tfrac{1}{2} \ln \left[ 2\pi np \left( 1 + \frac{x}{np} \right) \right]$$

$$+ (np + x) \ln p + (nq - x) \ln q \qquad (22)$$

Since $x/nq$ and $x/np$ are very small compared to unity, a MacLaurin series expansion of $\ln (1 - x/nq)$ and $\ln (1 + x/np)$ is possible with only the first two terms in the series used, that is,

$$\ln \left( 1 - \frac{x}{nq} \right) = \left( -\frac{x}{nq} \right) - \frac{x^2}{n^2 q^2} \qquad (23)$$

$$\ln \left( 1 + \frac{x}{np} \right) = \frac{x}{np} + \frac{x^2}{n^2 p^2} \qquad (24)$$

If equations 23 and 24 are substituted into equation 22 and the small convergent terms dropped, it can be easily shown that

$$\ln p_w{}^r = -\tfrac{1}{2} \ln (2\pi npq) - \frac{x^2}{2npq} \qquad (25)$$

or

$$p_w{}^r = \frac{1}{\sqrt{2\pi npq}} \exp \left( \frac{-x^2}{2npq} \right) \qquad (26)$$

Since $\sigma = \sqrt{npq}$ and $x = (r - \bar{r})$ (see equations 17 and 18)

$$p_w{}^r = \frac{1}{\sigma\sqrt{2\pi}} \exp\left[\frac{-(r - \bar{r})^2}{2\sigma^2}\right] \tag{27}$$

Equation 27 represents the Gaussian distribution function, has a continuous probability density function, and has dimensions, whereas equation 3, the binomial distribution function, represents a discrete probability depending on a fixed number of independent trials and is dimensionless. Since

$$\int_{-\infty}^{+\infty} (p_w{}^r)\, dr = 1 \tag{28}$$

then *all* objects must be counted and the probability for a given object having a specific value for property $w$ approaches zero.

The probability that any given object has a value less than or equal to $|K\sigma|$ for property $w$ is

$$\int_{-K\sigma}^{K\sigma} (p_w{}^r)\, dr = 2 \int_{0}^{K\sigma} (p_w{}^r)\, dr \tag{29}$$

Thus, the probability that any given object has a value greater than $K\sigma$ is

$$\int_{-\infty}^{\infty} (p_w{}^r)\, dr - \int_{-K\sigma}^{K\sigma} (p_w{}^r)\, dr = 2 \int_{K\sigma}^{\infty} (p_w{}^r)\, dr \tag{30}$$

Substitute $\alpha$ for $(r - \bar{r})/\sigma$ in equation 27; then,

$$2 \int_{K\sigma}^{\infty} (p_w{}^r)\, dr = \sqrt{\frac{2}{\pi}} \int_{K}^{\infty} [\exp(-\alpha^2/2)]\, d\alpha \tag{31}$$

It should be noted that the distribution represented in equation 31 has a mean of zero and that $K$ can be any number from zero to infinity.

The right-hand side of equation 31 can be evaluated for various

TABLE 4-1

Number of Standard Deviations K versus Probability of Occurrence

| Number of $K$'s | Probability of Absolute Error | Confidence (percent) |
|---|---|---|
| 0 | 1.00 | 0 |
| 0.674 | 0.50 | 50 |
| 1 | 0.32 | 68 |
| 2 | 0.046 | 95.4 |
| 3 | 0.002 | 99.8 |
| 4 | 0.00006 | 99.94 |

values of $K$, with some of the results given in Table 4-1. There, $0.674\sigma$ is called the *"probable error"* because the probability of an error greater than this quantity is $\frac{1}{2}$.

## THE LOG-NORMAL DISTRIBUTION LAW AND ITS MODIFICATIONS

### General Remarks

The statistical law most popular with physicists and chemists is the "Gaussian normal law," equation 27. As early as 1879, however, Galton (1) realized that it can lead to absurdities in many cases and gave the following example: if the normal law is applicable to the height of races of men, then the existence of giants whose height is more than double the mean height of their race, implies the possibility of the existence of dwarfs whose stature is less than nothing at all. Kottler (2) gives an excellent discussion of why the "Gaussian normal law" or "truncated" normal law or the Rosin-Rammler law (3) cannot be applied to particle size distribution, and the arguments can be simply condensed into the fact that it is impossible to have particles of a negative dimension, as evidently would be implied by the "Gaussian normal law."

The log-normal distribution law has been applied by several authors (4–11) to the distribution of sizes of particles obtained by crystallization and/or crushing. Hatch (12) and later Ames et al. (11) showed that if the particle size distribution gives a straight line on a number basis, when plotted on log probability graph paper, the size distribution by weight or surface area is a parallel straight line on the same coordinates.

### Derivation

Kottler (8) and Irani (13) have treated particle size distributions from a fruitful kinetic point of view. In general, it can be assumed that the size $M$ of a particle grows or diminishes according to the equation

$$\frac{dM}{dt} = \Phi(M) \tag{32}$$

where $\Phi(M)$ can be expressed as

$$\Phi(M) = K\,\frac{(M - M_0)(M_\infty - M)}{(M_\infty - M_0)} \tag{33}$$

$M_0$ and $M_\infty$ are the minimum and maximum sizes formed respectively, and $K$ is a velocity constant of formation that can be either positive or negative depending on whether the particulates are growing or are being destroyed. It is significant to note that as $M$ approaches either $M_0$ or $M_\infty$ it becomes time independent because $\Phi(M)$ becomes zero.

Since time does not have any starting point, the time units for growth or destruction can be either lengthened or shortened arbitrarily. This results in a justification for assuming that times of growth or destruction of particulates are normally distributed. Assuming a unit standard deviation, the normal distribution of time is represented by

$$f(t) = \frac{1}{\sqrt{2\pi}} \exp\left(\frac{-t^2}{2}\right) \tag{34}$$

If equations 32 and 33 are combined, then

$$t = a + b \ln \frac{(M - M_0)(M_\infty - M_0)}{(M_\infty - M)} \tag{35}$$

where $a$ and $b$ are constants. And from equations 34 and 35

$$f(M) = \frac{1}{\sqrt{2\pi}\ln\sigma} \exp\left\{-\left[\ln\frac{\dfrac{(M - M_0)(M_\infty - M_0)}{(M_\infty - M)\overline{M}}}{\sqrt{2}\ln\sigma}\right]^2\right\} \tag{36}$$

where $\sigma$ and $\overline{M}$ can be assumed for the time being to be arbitrary constants related to $a$ and $b$.

### Discussion

If the special case is considered, where $M_0 \simeq 0$ and $M_\infty$ is very large, equation 36 reduces to the *simple* log-normal distribution law:

$$f(M) = \frac{1}{\sqrt{2\pi}\ln\sigma} \exp\left\{-\left[\frac{\ln(M/\overline{M})}{\sqrt{2}\ln\sigma}\right]^2\right\} \tag{37}$$

The fraction $F$ of material that lies between sizes $M_1$ and $M_2$ is given by

$$F = \frac{1}{\sqrt{2\pi}\ln\sigma} \int_{\ln M_1}^{\ln M_2} f(M)\, d\ln M \tag{38}$$

If we let

$$z = \frac{\ln(M/\overline{M})}{\sqrt{2}\ln\sigma} \tag{39}$$

then 
$$d\ln M = \sqrt{2}\ln\sigma\, dz \tag{40}$$

and equation 38 becomes

$$F = \frac{1}{\sqrt{\pi}} \int_{z_1}^{z_2} \exp(-z^2)\, dz \tag{41}$$

If we choose to find the fraction of the particles below $\overline{M}$, we set

$M_1 = 0$ and $M_2 = \overline{M}$, for which equation 41 becomes

$$F_{0-\overline{M}} \frac{1}{\sqrt{\pi}} \int_{-\infty}^{0} \exp\left(-z^2\right) dz = \frac{1}{2\sqrt{\pi}} \Gamma\left(\frac{1}{2}\right) = \frac{1}{2} \qquad (42)$$

We can also compute the fraction of the material that lies between $\overline{M}$ and $\sigma\overline{M}$ using the transformation in equation 41:

$$F_{\overline{M}-\sigma\overline{M}} = \frac{1}{\sqrt{\pi}} \int_{0}^{\frac{1}{2}} \exp\left(-z^2\right) dz \qquad (43)$$

A MacLaurin expansion of $\exp\left(-z^2\right)$ yields a rapidly convergent series:

$$F_{\overline{M}-\sigma\overline{M}} = \frac{1}{\sqrt{\pi}} \left[ z - \frac{z^3}{3} + \frac{z^5}{10} - \frac{z^7}{21} \cdots \right]_{0}^{\frac{1}{2}} = 0.3413 \qquad (44)$$

In a similar way it can be shown that

$$F_{(\overline{M}/\sigma)-\overline{M}} = 0.3413 \qquad (45)$$

From equations 42, 44, and 45, it is therefore concluded that $\overline{M}$ and $\sigma$ are not arbitrary constants, but really represent important parameters of the distribution, namely, the geometric mean size and geometric standard deviation, respectively. Therefore we can now define $\overline{M}$ and $\sigma$. $\overline{M}$, the geometric mean size, is

$$\overline{M} = \sqrt[n]{M_1 \cdot M_2 \cdots M_n} \qquad (46)$$

or

$$\log \overline{M} = \frac{\sum\limits_{i=1}^{i=n} (n_i \log M_i)}{\Sigma n_i}$$

and

$$\log \sigma = \sqrt{\frac{\sum\limits_{i=1}^{i=n} n_i (\log M_i - \log \overline{M})^2}{\sum\limits_{i=1}^{i=n} n_i}} \qquad (47)$$

From equation 46 it is evident that $\sigma$ is unitless and that the minimum value it can have is one, which occurs if $M_i = M_j$, meaning that all the particles are of the same size. We can also define $\overline{M}$ as the value of $M$ at which 50% of the material is greater than, and 50% smaller than, the stated size. $\sigma$ on the other hand is the ratio of the size at 15.87% probability to that at 50%, or the ratio at 50% probability to that at 84.13%.

The relations we have mentioned are extensively used in the analysis of particle size data. This is natural, because if a distribution is truly log-normal, we need report only $\overline{M}$ and $\sigma$ and the whole distribution function can be defined.

## Averages of Different Order and Weighting in Log-Normal Distributions

We first wish to express the averages $\mu_i$ of a log-normal distribution and later show the physical significance of combinations of these averages:

$$\mu_1 = \frac{\Sigma n_i M_i}{\Sigma n_i} = \frac{1}{\sqrt{2\pi} \ln \sigma} \int_0^{\infty} M \exp\left[\frac{-(\ln M - \ln \overline{M})^2}{2 \ln^2 \sigma}\right] \cdot d \ln M \quad (48)$$

$$\mu_2 = \frac{\Sigma n_i M_i^2}{\Sigma n_i} = \frac{1}{\sqrt{2\pi} \ln \sigma} \int_0^{\infty} M^2 \exp\left[\frac{-(\ln M - \ln \overline{M})^2}{2 \ln^2 \sigma}\right] \cdot d \ln M \quad (49)$$

$$\mu_j = \frac{\Sigma n_i M_i^{\,j}}{\Sigma n_i} = \frac{1}{\sqrt{2\pi} \ln \sigma} \int_0^{\infty} M^j \exp\left[\frac{-(\ln M - \ln \overline{M})^2}{2 \ln^2 \sigma}\right] \cdot d \log M$$
$$(50)$$

To integrate 48 we make substitutions 39 and 40.

$$\mu_1 = \frac{\overline{M}}{\sqrt{\pi}} \int_{-\infty}^{\infty} \exp\left[\sqrt{2}(\ln \sigma)z - z^2\right] dz \quad (51)$$

Now make the transformation

$$y = z - \frac{\ln \sigma}{\sqrt{2}} \quad (52)$$

$$\mu_1 = \frac{\overline{M} \exp\left(\frac{1}{2} \ln^2 \sigma\right)}{\sqrt{\pi}} \int_{-\infty}^{\infty} \exp\left(-y^2\right) dy \quad (53)$$

From equations 42 and 53 we therefore show that

$$\mu_1 = \exp\left(\ln \overline{M} + \tfrac{1}{2} \ln^2 \sigma\right) \quad (54)$$

In a manner similar to the one we have shown, it is easy to show that

$$\mu_2 = \frac{\sum\limits_{i=1}^{i=n} n_i M_i^2}{\Sigma n_i} = \exp\left(2 \ln \overline{M} + 2 \ln^2 \sigma\right) \quad (55)$$

$$\mu_3 = \frac{\sum\limits_{i=1}^{i=n} n_i M_i^3}{\Sigma n_i} = \exp\left(3 \ln \overline{M} + 4.5 \ln^2 \sigma\right) \quad (56)$$

$$\mu_4 = \frac{\sum\limits_{i=1}^{i=n} n_i M_i^4}{\Sigma n_i} = \exp\left(4 \ln \overline{M} + 8 \ln^2 \sigma\right) \quad (57)$$

## The Relations between the Various Average Sizes of Nonuniform Particulate Substances

In what follows we assume that we have measured and calculated $\overline{M}_n$ and $\sigma_n$, the geometric mean size and geometric standard deviation on a number basis, respectively, and show how to calculate the other average sizes. Once this is done it becomes apparent how to convert one set of size measurements into a different set that is more closely related to the physical variables in which we are interested. Because of the nature of the log-normal distribution law, it is evident that the geometric standard deviations on a number or count basis, weight basis, surface area basis, etc., are equal.

The arithmetic mean size $\overline{M}_{a\alpha}$ is defined as

$$\overline{M}_{a\alpha} = \frac{\sum\limits_{i=1}^{i=n} n_i M_i}{\sum\limits_{i=1}^{i=n} n_i} \tag{58}$$

where $\alpha$ denotes any of the weighting methods, for example, number or weight distributions, whereas $\overline{M}_{sa}$, the size on an external-surface area basis, is

$$\overline{M}_{sa} = \left( \frac{\sum\limits_{i=1}^{i=n} n_i M_i^2}{\sum\limits_{i=1}^{i=n} n_i} \right)^{\frac{1}{2}} \tag{59}$$

and $\overline{M}_v$, the size on a volume basis, is

$$\overline{M}_v = \left( \frac{\sum\limits_{i=1}^{i=n} n_i M_i^3}{\sum\limits_{i=1}^{i=n} n_i} \right)^{\frac{1}{3}} \tag{60}$$

For a log-normal distribution, if equations 54, 55, and 56 are combined with 58, 59, and 60, it is apparent that

$$\ln \overline{M}_{a\alpha} = \ln \overline{M}_\alpha + \tfrac{1}{2} \ln^2 \sigma_\alpha \tag{61}$$

$$\ln \overline{M}_{sa} = \ln \overline{M}_n + \ln^2 \sigma_n \tag{62}$$

$$\ln \overline{M}_v = \ln \overline{M}_n + 1.5 \ln^2 \sigma_n \tag{63}$$

The size on a specific surface area basis, $\overline{M}_{sv}$:

$$\overline{M}_{sv} = \frac{\sum\limits_{i=1}^{i=n} n_i M_i^3}{\sum\limits_{i=1}^{i=n} n_i M_i^2} \tag{64}$$

is evidently arrived at as follows:

$$\ln \overline{M}_{sv} = \ln \frac{\sum\limits_{i=1}^{i=n} n_i M_i^3}{\sum\limits_{i=1}^{i=n} n_i} - \ln \frac{\sum\limits_{i=1}^{i=n} n_i M_i^2}{\sum\limits_{i=1}^{i=n} n_i}$$

$$= \ln \overline{M}_n + 2.5 \ln^2 \sigma_n \tag{65}$$

Finally, we wish to derive the relation between the geometric mean sizes on a weight and number basis.

The arithmetic mean of a weight distribution, $\overline{M}_{ag}$, is given by equation 61

$$\ln \overline{M}_{ag} = \ln \overline{M}_g + \tfrac{1}{2} \ln^2 \sigma_g \tag{66}$$

Nevertheless, assuming $dM\alpha/d\rho = 0$ where $\rho$ is the particle density and realizing that the arithmetic mean size by weight is the sum of the weights of particles of a certain size (sieve opening) multiplied by the corresponding size and divided by the total weight, we see that

$$\overline{M}_{ag} = \frac{\sum\limits_{i=1}^{i=n} (\rho n_i M_i^3) M_i}{\sum\limits_{i=1}^{i=n} \rho n_i M_i^3} = \frac{\sum\limits_{i=1}^{i=n} n_i M_i^4}{\sum\limits_{i=1}^{i=n} n_i M_i^3} \tag{67}$$

Therefore, from equations 56 and 57:

$$\ln \overline{M}_{ag} = \ln \overline{M}_n + 3.5 \ln^2 \sigma_n \tag{68}$$

Since $\sigma_n = \sigma_g$, combining equations 66 and 68 yields

$$\ln \overline{M}_g = \ln \overline{M}_n + 3.0 \ln^2 \sigma_n \tag{69}$$

Table 4-2 summarizes the relations between the various sizes. In using these transformations it is very important to keep in mind that they are only correct *provided* a log-normal distribution exists. In cases where it is hard to decide whether or not a log-normal distribution is obeyed, it is advisable to use the defining equations in the third column for the sizes rather than the relations shown in the last column of Table 4-2.

### Abnormal Log-Normal Distributions

In many cases the plot of the particle size distribution is not a straight line on log probability graph paper, so that the simple log-normal distribution does not fit the data. We now present an interpre-

TABLE 4-2

The Relations between the Average Sizes of Nonuniform Particulate Substances,
Provided a Log-Normal Distribution Is Obeyed

| Average Size | Symbol | Mathematical Definition (Summation between $i = 1$ and $i = n$) | Equivalent Natural Logarithms in Terms of Statistical Parameters of Distribution Curve by Number, $\overline{M}_n$ and $\sigma_n$ |
|---|---|---|---|
| Geometric mean, on weight basis | $\overline{M}_g$ | $\dfrac{\Sigma n_i M_i^4}{\Sigma n_i M_i^3}$ | $\ln \overline{M}_n + 3.0 \ln^2 \sigma_n$ |
| Arithmetic mean, on number basis | $\overline{M}_{an}$ | $\dfrac{\Sigma n_i M_i}{\Sigma n_i}$ | $\ln \overline{M}_n + 0.5 \ln^2 \sigma_n$ |
| Surface area | $\overline{M}_{sa}$ | $\left(\dfrac{\Sigma n_i M_i^2}{\Sigma n_i}\right)^{1/2}$ | $\ln \overline{M}_n + 1.0 \ln^2 \sigma_n$ |
| Volume | $\overline{M}_v$ | $\left(\dfrac{\Sigma n_i M_i^3}{\Sigma n_i}\right)^{1/3}$ | $\ln \overline{M}_n + 1.5 \ln^2 \sigma_n$ |
| Specific surface area | $\overline{M}_{sv}$ | $\dfrac{\Sigma n_i M_i^3}{\Sigma n_i M_i^2}$ | $\ln \overline{M}_n + 2.5 \ln^2 \sigma_n$ |

tation and a discussion of basic cases whereby a modified log-normal distribution is obeyed. The interpretations are particularly useful for powders obtained through fractionation, spray drying, and/or controlled formation. The treatment is also useful in the measurement of particle size through the use of the Tyndall spectra (the variation of scattered light with wavelength) which Sinclair and La Mer (14), Heller et al. (15, 16), and Loebel (17) have shown to be powerful for monodisperse systems and that it would be more generally applicable if the general distribution function of the particle sizes had been known a priori.

Kottler (18) has presented a rigorous but time-consuming algebraic treatment of the data typified by those encountered (19, 21) during studies of photographic emulsions, where it was found that the simple log-normal distribution did not fit the data. Although the treatment that will be presented here is as rigorous as Kottler's, it is more general and has been designed to be less time consuming by using certain graphical properties of the plots of the size distribution. Loveland (19–21) had previously arrived at a similar conclusion.

**Limited and Unlimited Growth**

Equation 36 can be integrated to yield $P$, the percent greater than size $M$:

$$P = 100 \int_M^\infty f(M) \, d \ln \frac{M - M_0}{M_\infty - M_0}$$

$$= 50 - 100 \operatorname{erf} \left[ \frac{\ln \dfrac{(M - M_0)(M_\infty - M_0)}{\overline{M}(M_\infty - M)}}{\ln \sigma} \right] \tag{70}$$

where $\overline{M}$ is the geometric mean size of the parent distribution, and erf is the error integral. The special cases of equation 70 are as follows:

*Case 1.* If $M_0 = 0$ and $M_\infty \to \infty$, then equation 70 reduces to the *simple* log-normal distribution that gives a straight line on the log probability axis as shown in Fig. 4-1 for $\overline{M} = 10$ microns and $\sigma = 2$. This case corresponds to unlimited formation.

*Case 2.* Figure 4-1 also illustrates the case where $\overline{M} = 10$ microns, $\sigma = 2$, $M_\infty \to \infty$, but $M_0 = 7$ microns. The curve is shown to be asymptotic to 7 microns; the points are calculated from equation 70. Here if $(M - M_0)$ rather than $M$ had been plotted on log probability paper, a

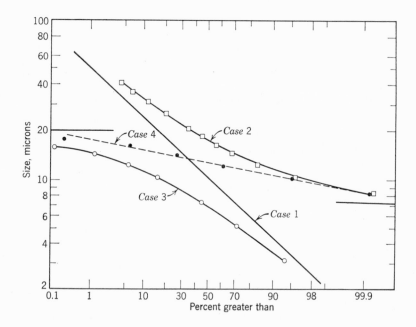

FIG. 4-1. Limited and unlimited growth.

straight line would have been obtained. The case with $M_0 > 0$ has been used by several authors, of whom we can mention Sheppard et al. (22) and Gaddum (23).

*Case 3.* When $M_\infty \neq \infty$, a plot similar to the one shown as *case 3* in Fig. 4-1 is obtained. The curve is always asymptotic toward the upper-limit size, as illustrated in Fig. 4-1 for $M_\infty = 20$ microns, $\overline{M} = 10$ microns, and $\sigma = 2$. If $MM_\infty/(M_\infty - M)$ rather than $M$ had been plotted on log probability paper, a straight line would have been obtained.

*Case 4.* If $M_0 = 7$ microns, $M_\infty = 20$ microns, $\overline{M} = 10$ microns, and $\sigma = 2$, the plot shown in Fig. 4-1 is obtained. The interesting point here is that similar plots do not deviate significantly from a straight line (shown dotted), and when the data are obtained experimentally it is not justifiable to use the four-parameter fit we have indicated, but rather *two* new parameters, namely $\overline{M}' = 12.6$ microns and $\sigma' = 1.8$. The importance of this conclusion is that although most powders are formed according to the kinetic equation describing *case 4*, the evaluation of experimental data indicates a simple unlimited-growth-type log-normal distribution. Thus, although a particular substance under specified conditions has a specific rate constant $K$, the values of $\overline{M}'$ and $\sigma$ can be varied by changing $M_0$, for example, through nucleation or finer grinding, and $M_\infty$, for example, through changing the time function by shortening or prolonging the particle formation period.

For *cases 2* and *3* $M_0$ and $M_\infty$ are easily located from the asymptotical character of the curve.

### Artificial Distributions

*Cases 2* through *4* cover the modifications in the log-normal distribution due to variables controlling the formation of the particles. After formation, however, powders are generally tampered with, either through dust separation by cyclones or removal of coarse particles (or combinations of these and similar operations) as described in *cases 5–7* and illustrated in Fig. 4-2.

*Case 5.* If particles below a certain size $M_l$ are removed, for example, cyclone dust removal, a curve asymptoting toward $M_l$ is obtained. In Fig. 4-2, $M_l = 10$ microns, $\overline{M} = 32$ microns, $\sigma = 4$.

*Case 6.* If particles above a certain size $M_m$ are removed, for example, by precise sieving or collecting the fines in a cyclone, a curve asymptoting toward $M_m$ is obtained. In Fig. 4-2, $M_m = 100$ microns, $\overline{M} = 32$ microns, $\sigma = 4$.

*Case 7.* This is a combination of *cases 5* and *6*. In Fig. 4-2, $M_m = 100$

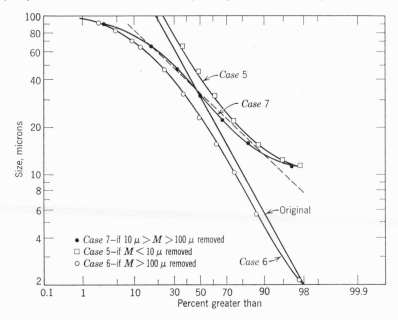

FIG. 4-2. Artificial separation.

microns, $M_l = 10$ microns, $\overline{M} = 32$ microns, and $\sigma = 4$. *Case 7* is similar to *case 4* in that a straight line, shown dashed in Fig. 4-2, can adequately represent the data shown by the solid line.

The original distribution can be obtained for *case 6* by first estimating the "percent finer than" $100 - \mathring{P}$ that would have been observed had there been no removal of particles bigger than the size exhibiting an asymptote, and then dividing the "percent finer than" by $100/\mathring{P}$ at various sizes to obtain the original distribution exhibiting log normal behavior. The value of $\mathring{P}$ can be estimated within $10\%$ by extrapolating the straight line observed at small sizes to the size exhibiting an asymptote. If the chosen value of $\mathring{P}$ does not render a straight line, the fit can be improved by either increasing or decreasing $\mathring{P}$, as illustrated in Fig. 4-3. The data shown in Fig. 4-3 are for a sample of clay that had been treated to remove large particles; it is shown that by making only two approximations we can obtain the *parent* size distribution curve and also the amount of clay above 45 microns that had been removed.

*Case 5* can be treated in the same manner as *case 6* except that $\mathring{P}$ is used in place of $100 - \mathring{P}$.

A question that arises at this point is whether *cases 5, 6,* and *7* are

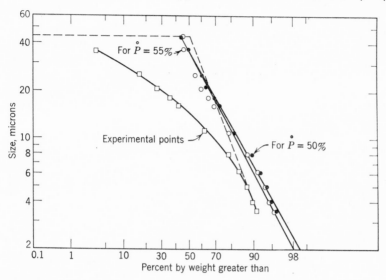

FIG. 4-3. Estimation of $P$.

significantly different from *2, 3,* and *4.* It turns out that they are different and that they can be easily distinguished using a histogram plot. For *cases 2, 3,* and *4* the size frequency plot has a definite slope at $M_0$ and $M_\infty$ as compared with *cases 5, 6,* and *7,* where a discontinuity in the size frequency curve is obtained at $M_l$ and $M_m$. This phenomenon is illustrated in Fig. 4-4, for *cases 3* and *6,* where it can be easily seen

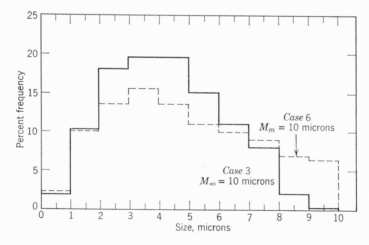

FIG. 4-4. Histograms for *cases 3* and *6* with $\overline{M} = 6.5$ and $\sigma = 2.31$.

that although $M_m$ and $M_\infty$ were identical for two particular distributions, the two cases gave histograms exceedingly different near $M_m$ and $M_\infty$.

### Heterogeneous (Multimodel) Distributions

Several empirical equations have been proposed for fitting bimodal distributions, for example, the algebraic equation suggested by Dallavalle et al. (24). A general treatment is as follows:

Heterogeneous (multimodal) particle size distributions generally arise either from mixing powders or from the existence of different rates and boundary conditions during the formation of the particles, for example, different-shape particles and/or crystal habits. Thus, if we had an $n$th-modal distribution, meaning $n$ populations, then $P$ could be expressed as

$$P = 50 - 100 \sum_{i=1}^{i=n} f_i \operatorname{erf}\left[\frac{\ln \dfrac{(M - M_{0i})(M_{\infty i} - M_{0i})}{\overline{M}_i(M_{\infty i} - M)}}{\ln \sigma_i}\right] \qquad (71)$$

where the subscript $i$ refers to a particular population. In most practical cases, however, $n = 2$, and in the following special cases it will be also assumed that $M_{0i} = 0$ and $M_{\infty i} \to \infty$. In both cases a good estimate of $\overline{M}_1$ and $\overline{M}_2$ can be made from the size frequency histogram as illustrated by Whitby (25) for a sample of flour.

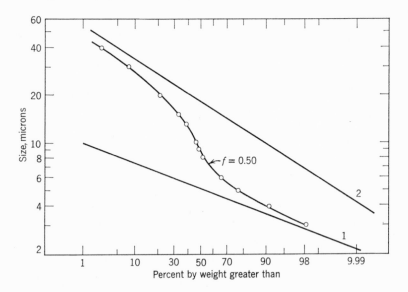

FIG. 4-5. Heterogeneous distribution, *case 8a*.

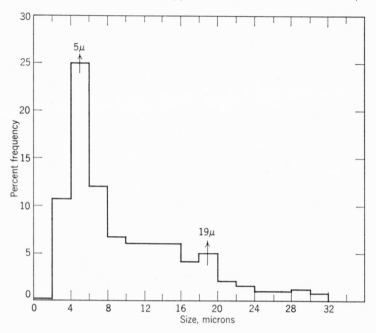

FIG. 4-6. Histogram of heterogeneous distribution, *case 8a*.

*Case 8a.* If the parent distribution curves do not intersect on a log probability plot, a curve similar to that shown in Fig. 4-5 is obtained. The characteristic of the plot is that it asymptotes at its upper and lower levels to two nonhorizontal lines, these lines being the parent distributions (equation 71).

As an example, the experimental points shown in Fig. 4-5 are treated as follows to obtain the parent distributions. The data are plotted on a size frequency histogram as shown in Fig. 4-6 to obtain $\overline{M}_1 = 5$ microns and $\overline{M}_2 = 19$ microns. Equation 71 becomes

$$P = 50 - 100\,f\,\mathrm{erf}\left[\frac{\ln\,(M/5)}{\ln\,\sigma_1}\right] - 100\,(1-f)\,\mathrm{erf}\left[\frac{\ln\,(M/19)}{\ln\,\sigma_2}\right] \quad (72)$$

where $f$ is the fraction $f_1$. The next step is to obtain a first approximation of $\sigma_1$ and $\sigma_2$ from the asymptotes of the experimental points and compute the value of $f$ at various values of $P$. If the value of $f$ turns out to be independent of $P$ and $M$, the estimated values of $\sigma_1$ and $\sigma_2$ are accurate. Otherwise successive approximations are necessary. Table 4-3 demonstrates the relative constancy of $f$ for the data in Figs. 4-5 and 4-6 after only two successive approximations to obtain $\sigma_1$ and

TABLE 4-3

Heterogeneous Distribution Example for *Case 8a*

| $M$ (microns) | $P_{\text{meas}}$ | $f_{\text{calc}}{}^{a}$ |
|---|---|---|
| 3 | 98.3 | 0.85 |
| 4 | 91 | 0.51 |
| 5 | 77 | 0.46 |
| 6 | 65 | 0.45 |
| 8 | 52 | 0.48 |
| 9 | 49 | 0.48 |
| 10 | 46 | 0.51 |
| 13 | 39 | 0.51 |
| 15 | 33 | 0.52 |
| 20 | 21 | 0.54 |
| 30 | 7.5 | 0.53 |
| 40 | 2.5 | 0.46 |
| Average[b] | | $0.50 \pm 0.03$ |

[a] Assuming $\overline{M}_1 = 5$ microns, $\overline{M}_2 = 19$ microns, $\sigma_1 = 1.28$, $\sigma_2 = 1.56$.
[b] Ignoring the value at $M = 3$ microns.

$\sigma_2$. The calculated $f$ values at the lowest values of $M$ tend to be off because of the high dependence on $100 - P$ shown in equation **72**; at low values of $M$, the value of $P$ usually cannot be determined with enough

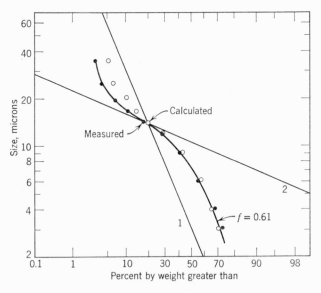

FIG. 4-7. Heterogeneous distribution, *case 8b*.

accuracy, so that the calculated $f$ values can be ignored in that region.

*Case 8b.* If the parent distribution curves intersect on a log probability plot, a curve similar to that shown in Fig. 4-7 is obtained. In this case the experimental points asymptote at both ends of the distribution toward the original parent distribution with the higher $\sigma$. The asymptotes do not approach specific size values as was observed in *case 8a*. The point of inflection, however, turns out to be an important point since both parent curves must go through it. Therefore, to resolve the example given in Fig. 4-7, the data are first plotted on a histogram (as was done in Fig. 4-6) to obtain $\overline{M}_1$ and $\overline{M}_2$, which in this case turn out to be 3.0 and 10.5 microns respectively. The point of inflection can then be located very accurately by drawing the tangents to the curve and locating the point of maximum change of slope, 14 microns in this example. $\overline{M}_1$ and $\overline{M}_2$ are located on 50% probability and connected to the point of inflection by straight lines to obtain $\sigma_1 = 6.0$ and $\sigma_2 = 1.47$. The values of $f$ are then computed from equation 73 at various measured values of $P$ and $M$:

$$P = 50 - 100\, f\, \text{erf} \left[ \frac{\ln\,(M/3)}{\ln 6} \right] - 100\,(1 - f)\, \text{erf} \left[ \frac{\ln\,(M/10.5)}{\ln 1.47} \right] \quad (73)$$

The calculated values of $f$ are shown in Table 4-4 and are erratic for the low values of $P$ because $f$ is highly dependent on the measured

### TABLE 4-4

#### Heterogeneous Distribution Example for Case 8b

| $M$ (microns) | $P_{\text{meas}}$ | $f_{\text{calc}}$[a] | $P_{\text{calc}}$[b] | $\Delta$[c] |
|---|---|---|---|---|
| 3 | 71 | 0.58 | 69.0 | 2.0 |
| 4 | 66 | 0.60 | 65.3 | 0.7 |
| 6 | 56 | 0.63 | 57.6 | 1.6 |
| 9 | 42 | 0.62 | 42.3 | 1.3 |
| 12 | 28 | 0.63 | 28.3 | 0.3 |
| 14 | 20 | (0.77) | 20.4 | 0.4 |
| 17 | 10 | (0.06) | 14.1 | 4.1 |
| 20 | 6.5 | — | 10.8 | 4.3 |
| 24 | 4.0 | — | 8.5 | 3.5 |
| 35 | 3.0 | — | 5.1 | 2.1 |

Average[d] $0.61 \pm 0.02$

[a] Assuming $\overline{M}_1 = 3.0$ microns, $\overline{M}_2 = 10.5$ microns, $\sigma_1 = 6.0$, $\sigma_2 = 1.47$.
[b] Assuming note $a$, and $f = 0.61$.
[c] $P_{\text{calc}} - P_{\text{meas}}$.
[d] For 14 microns $> M > 3$ microns.

values of $P$; unavoidable experimental errors in $P$ can cause large variations in $f$, as shown for $M = 14$ microns and $M = 17$ microns. If the average value of $f$ is taken, however, and $P_{calc}$ is compared with $P_{meas}$, the average difference is only $\pm2\%$, which is definitely within the $\pm5\%$ for the experimental error. Thus from only one estimate an excellent resolution was obtained. For all the resolutions we have encountered it was not necessary in any situation to make more than three approximations. Table 4-5 shows the agreement between calculated $f$ and known values of $f$ for synthetic powdered mixtures.

TABLE 4-5

Heterogeneous Distribution

| $f_{calc}$[a] | $f_{known}$[a] |
|---|---|
| 0.50 | 0.50 |
| 0.61 | 0.67 |
| 0.30 | 0.33 |
| 0.85 | 0.80 |
| 0.18 | 0.20 |
| 0.72 | 0.75 |
| 0.66 | 0.67 |

[a] From synthetically mixing known weights of two powders.

In some rare cases where *limited growth* distributions are combined, the treatments presented for *cases 8a* and *8b* do not apply directly, and the complexity of the problem of resolution increases exponentially.

### Number-Surface-Weight Distributions

As was discussed previously, the value of $P$ depends to a large extent on whether it refers to a number, surface, or weight basis. Thus, if we had the hypothetical case of equal numbers of spherical particles having 1 micron and 10-micron diameters, then the contribution of the small particles to the mixture is $\frac{1}{2}$ on a number basis, $\frac{1}{101}$ on an external-surface basis, and $\frac{1}{1001}$ on a weight basis. When abnormal distributions are encountered they may be important on a number basis and not on a surface or weight basis, and vice versa. Figure 4-8 illustrates this point clearly. The number-size distribution shows definite bimodality although the weight convert of the data and the measured weight-size distribution agree with one another and show lognormal behavior in all practical regions. The dotted line shown in Fig. 4-8 is where the weight-size distribution starts deviating from a

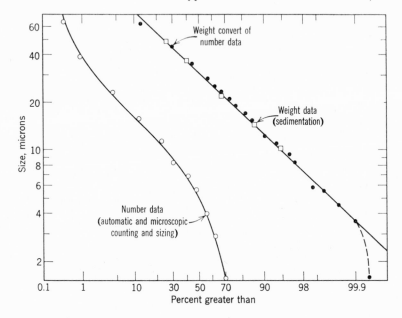

FIG. 4-8. Comparison of number- and weight-size distributions.

straight line. Many other similar examples have been observed for *cases 2–8*.

## OTHER DISTRIBUTION LAWS

Although the most widely applicable distribution law is the log-normal or one of its modifications, several empirical equations have been proposed. These empirical equations are successful in representing the data only when the simple log-normal law is not obeyed. Rather than try to fit the data to a rigorous, modified log-normal distribution law involving three or four parameters, several investigators fitted very specific equations with only two parameters.

For a very few powders whose minimum size is not close to zero, the distribution of the sizes seems to approach the normal probability distribution function. When this happens, the cumulative curve plots as a straight line of particle size is plotted on a linear scale and cumulative percent oversize, or undersize, is represented on the probability scale.

Materials that show an approximately arithmetic normal distribution are relatively rare and are found chiefly among substances produced by a chemical process in which the particles tend to a uniform size (26) rather than those produced by crushing or grinding. An example is the data on zinc oxide reported by Green (27). Another interesting example, not directly related to particle size itself, is based on data by Daeves (28), where the size of a number of drilled holes whose nominal diameter was 15 mm was found to fit the normal-distribution law.

Roller (29), using what he called a purely inductive reasoning, proposed that

$$100 - P = aM^{1/2} \exp\left(\frac{-b}{M}\right) \tag{74}$$

where $a$ and $b$ are parameters. For unimodal distributions the plot of $\log\left[(100 - P)/M^{1/2}\right]$ versus $1/M$ yields a straight line; for mine coal and mine limestone, two intersecting lines resulted (29) that were presumed to represent a bimodal distribution. Equation 74 has not been found to be widely applicable.

Rosin and Rammler (3) proposed the distribution law

$$P' = 100 \exp\left(-\frac{M}{c}\right)^b \tag{75}$$

where $c$ and $b$ are constants and $P'$ is the percent of particles having a size larger than $M$. From equation 75 we note that

$$\ln \ln \frac{100}{P'} = b \ln \frac{M}{c}$$

and therefore, the plot of $\log 100/P'$ versus $M$ on a log-log grid should give a straight line, if the Rosin-Rammler distribution is obeyed. The Rosin-Rammler equation is strictly empirical and relies heavily on curve fitting, and has been found to be applicable only in the case of powdered coal having a small range in particle size. Even then a modified log-normal distribution equation can be shown to give just as good a fit. In addition, the Rosin-Rammler distribution cannot be conveniently used to obtain the various statistical measures (30) of the particle size distribution such as weight-mean size. For example, Langemann (31) had to go through extremely complicated integrations to compute specific surface areas.

There are several other intricate size distribution equations that are only applicable in extremely specialized cases. The distribution functions that were covered in this chapter have the widest application and are the most useful in describing particle size distributions.

**REFERENCES**

1. F. Galton, *Proc. Roy. Soc. (London)*, **29**, 365 (1879).
2. F. Kottler, *J. Franklin Inst.*, **250**, 339 (1950).

3. P. Rosin and E. Rammler, *J. Inst. Fuel*, **7**, 29 (1933).

4. P. Drinker, *J. Ind. Hyg. Tox.*, **7**, 305 (1925).

5. J. B. Austin, *Ind. Eng. Chem.* (*Anal. Ed.*), **11**, 334 (1939).

6. T. Hatch and S. Choate, *J. Franklin Inst.*, **207**, 369 (1933).

7. B. Epstein, *ibid.*, **244**, 471 (1947); *J. Appl. Phys.*, **19**, 140 (1948); *Ind. Eng. Chem.*, **40**, 2289 (1948).

8. F. Kottler, *J. Franklin Inst.*, **250**, 339 (1950); *ibid.*, **250**, 419 (1950).

9. G. W. Phelps and S. G. Maguire, *J. Am. Ceram. Soc.*, **40**, 403 (1957).

10. O. Menis, H. P. House, and C. M. Boyd, *ORNL 2345*, Chemistry-General, Oak Ridge, Tenn., Atomic Energy Commission Unclassified Report.

11. D. P. Ames, R. R. Irani, and C. F. Callis, *J. Phys. Chem.*, **63**, 531 (1959).

12. T. Hatch, *J. Franklin Inst.*, **215**, 27 (1933).

13. R. R. Irani, *J. Phys. Chem.*, **63**, 1603 (1959).

14. D. Sinclair and V. K. La Mer, *Chem. Rev.*, **44**, 245 (1949).

15. W. Heller and E. Vassy, *Phys. Rev.*, **63**, 65 (1943).

16. ———, *J. Chem. Phys.*, **14**, 565 (1946).

17. A. B. Loebel, *Ind. Eng. Chem.*, **51**, 118 (1959).

18. F. Kottler, *J. Phys. Chem.*, **56**, 442 (1952).

19. R. P. Loveland and A. P. H. Trivelli, *J. Franklin Inst.*, **204**, 193 (1927).

20. ———, *ibid.*, **204**, 377 (1927).

21. ———, *J. Phys. Chem.*, **51**, 1004 (1947).

22. S. E. Sheppard, E. D. Wightman, and A. P. H. Trivelli, *Phot. J.*, **49**, 134 (1925).

23. J. H. Gaddum, *Nature*, **156**, 463 (1945).

24. J. M. Dallavalle, C. Orr, and H. G. Blocker, *Ind. Eng. Chem.*, **43**, 1377 (1951).

25. K. T. Whitby, *Heating, Piping and Air Conditioning*, **27** (6), 139 (1955).

26. J. B. Austin, *Ind. Eng. Chem.* (*Anal. Ed.*), **11**, 334 (1939).

27. H. L. Green, *J. Franklin Inst.*, **192**, 637 (1921).

28. G. Daeves, *Praktische Grosszahl-Forschung*, VDI Verlag, Berlin, 1933.

29. P. S. Roller, *J. Franklin Inst.*, **223**, 609 (1937).

30. J. M. Dallavalle, *Micromeritics*, Pitman Publishing Corp., New York, second edition, 1948, p. 63.

31. H. Langemann, *Chem. Ingr. Tech.*, **27**, 27 (1955).

# chapter 5

# Sedimentation techniques

Sedimentation techniques utilize the dependence of the falling velocities of particles on their size. Hall (1) was the first to apply Stokes'
equation to the measurement of particle size. The application of Stokes'
equation to systems consisting of particles of various sizes was made
in 1911 by Svedberg and Estrup (2). During the last half-century many
modifications of these classical experiments have been introduced.

One of the common criticisms of sedimentation techniques is that
they are only valid for spherical particles under restricted conditions.
This criticism is too severe if due consideration is given to the con-
venience of reporting size rather than settling velocities. Thus particulate matter may be represented by a rate-of-sedimentation distribution
in a specific medium, and the distribution reported will be free of
theoretical assumptions. It is, however, more plausible and convenient
to report particle size distributions that, for all practical purposes, are
independent of the sedimentation medium.

## RATES OF SEDIMENTATION

### Driving Forces

Although many types of electrical and magnetic forces can be applied to particles, the ones we deal with here are those produced either
by a gravitational field or by a centrifugal field.

A rigid particle in suspension in a fluid is acted on by the force of
gravity and by the buoyant force of the medium. Both are proportional

to the volume of the particle, $V$, and the local acceleration due to gravity, $g$ (981 cm/sec$^2$ at sea level). The net force $G$, which is the sedimentation driving force, is

$$G = V(\rho_1 - \rho_2)g \tag{1}$$

where $\rho_1$ and $\rho_2$ are the densities of the particle and the medium respectively.

For a particle in a centrifugal field, the driving force $C$ is the difference between the centrifugal and the buoyant force:

$$C = mw^2 R \tag{2}$$

where $w$ is the angular velocity, $R$ is the distance of the particle from the center of rotation, and $m$ is the effective mass of the particle, so that

$$C = V(\rho_1 - \rho_2)\, w^2 R \tag{3}$$

Sometimes the particles in a medium become solvated and, of course, this adds to their weight and volume. The added solvent particles are, however, also buoyed by the surrounding medium. Therefore in computing the sedimentation driving force the two effects cancel one another, and normally solvation has no appreciable effect on the driving force.

## Resistance to Motion and Stokes' Law

Under the influence of driving forces a particle starts accelerating according to Newton's law and moving through the liquid with a finite velocity $v$. This motion, however, causes a new force to appear, namely, the resistance of the liquid to motion.

In 1849 Stokes (3) used the principles of hydrodynamics and several simplifying assumptions to derive the equation for the force of resistance to motion, $F$, of a sphere:

$$F = -3\pi\eta vd \tag{4}$$

where $d$ is the diameter of the sphere, $\eta$ is the viscosity of the fluid, and $v$ is the velocity of the particle. The detailed derivation is available in advanced physics books (4). It is important, although we do not give the detailed derivation, to discuss the pertinent limitations that are involved in it.

Equation 4 assumes an infinite coefficient of sliding friction, meaning that the solvent forms a continuum. Otherwise, the particles may slip between the molecules of the sedimentation fluid. The problem of slippage becomes pronounced when the size of the sedimenting particles approaches that of the solvent molecules. Although in most liquid sedimentation experiments slippage is unimportant, correction factors have been proposed (5). It has also been shown that slippage is more serious when sedimentation is carried out in the gaseous phase rather than in the liquid phase because then there are relatively large mean free paths for gaseous molecules (6).

Stokes' equation holds strictly only at extremely slow motion, also called laminar or streamline motion, and should be corrected in terms of higher powers of $v$, which become important as $v$ increases. Rose (7) showed that equation 4 is valid to within 1% if the Reynolds number Re does not exceed 0.1, where

$$\text{Re} = \frac{v\rho_2 d}{\eta} \tag{5}$$

For water at 25°C, it can be shown from equation 5 that for a powder with a particle density of 2.5 gm/cc, the upper limiting size for streamline motion is 50 microns. Of course, at about 50 microns Stokes' law does not abruptly cease to hold; rather, the introduced errors become significant. For example, at 120 microns there is a 15% error in the settling velocity of the system we have given if equation 4 is utilized by itself.

As the size of particles becomes smaller and smaller, the molecular bombardment to which they are subjected becomes more effective, whereas the forces of gravity and centrifugation become less dominating. Instead of pursuing a direct course through the fluid, the particles stagger and zigzag with Brownian displacement in a fashion similar to the random walk problem (8). The classic equation is

$$X^2 = \frac{2kTt}{3\pi\eta d} \tag{6}$$

where $X$ is the Brownian displacement, $k$ is Boltzmann's constant, $T$ is the temperature, and $t$ is the time. In gravitational sedimentation, Brownian motion becomes important only for particles smaller than 0.5 micron. For centrifugal sedimentation at thousands of revolutions per minute, the lower limit is around 0.01 micron.

When Stokes' law is utilized, the particulate concentration should not exceed 1% by volume. Otherwise, interference between the particles becomes important. In addition, the viscosity of the medium ceases to be that of the pure fluid (9). Experimental data (10) and theory (11) are available on sedimentation in flocculated and nonflocculated suspensions at relatively high concentrations.

Liquid droplets, such as those in an emulsion, can flow internally, so that the resistance to their motion is somewhat smaller than that predicted by equation 4, but the errors can be generally neglected (12). Nevertheless, the major problem in using sedimentation for emulsions is coalescence.

Thus Stokes' law is limiting and deviations from it are to be expected. The deviations, however, need not be significant when proper upper and lower size limits are considered and abided by.

## Nonspherical Particles

Although Stokes' frictional coefficient is only strictly applicable to perfectly spherical particles, it can be utilized for particles whose maximum-to-minimum-diameter ratio (13, 14) does not exceed 4. In addition, contrary to common belief and expectation, there is no torque at low velocities on nonspherical particles during sedimentation (15) no matter what their orientation is. Therefore, the resistance they encounter during sedimentation can be averaged out over all possible orientations and a single value of the resistance coefficient assigned (13-15). This average resistance coefficient is the one assigned to the size of the particle (13), so that equation 4 becomes

$$F = -3\pi\eta v M \qquad (7)$$

where $M$ is the size of the particle averaged over all possible orientations of settling. Obviously, if the shape of the particles is of primary importance, sedimentation experiments alone are inadequate in describing the system.

Another important general result of a study (15) of friction factors for nonspherical particles having the same total volume is that the resistance to motion is the smallest for a sphere and increases with the deviation from sphericity, that is, with increased dissymmetry. This leads to the conclusion that although for irregular particles the resistance is reduced in one direction through elongation, the increase of resistance to motion in other directions is greater, so that the overall resistance to motion is increased.

## Sedimentation in a Gravitational Field

It has been repeatedly observed that particles settling in a viscous medium will reach a constant terminal velocity, at which time the driving force becomes equal to the resistance:

$$V(\rho_1 - \rho_2)g = 3\pi\eta v M \qquad (8)$$

In addition,

$$V = \frac{\alpha\pi M^3}{6} \qquad (9)$$

where $\alpha = 1$ for a sphere, and from equations 8 and 9

$$M = \left[\frac{18\eta v}{\alpha(\rho_1 - \rho_2)g}\right]^{\frac{1}{2}} \tag{10}$$

When the particle deviates significantly from sphericity, that is, the maximum-to-minimum-diameter ratio exceeds about 6, and $\alpha$ is unknown, the value of $M$ from equation 10 is referred to as the Stokesian size.

Prior to the use of equation 10, we should establish that the equality in equation 8 is valid. For particles having a specific gravity of 2 settling in water at 25°C, the distance traveled prior to attaining the terminal velocity is given in Table 5-1 as calculated with the aid of equation 8. It is apparent that particles smaller than 200 microns attain the terminal velocity almost instantaneously. Therefore equation 10 becomes

$$M = \left[\frac{18\eta h}{\alpha t(\rho_1 - \rho_2)g}\right]^{\frac{1}{2}} \tag{11}$$

where $h$ is the distance settled, $t$ is the time of settling, and $\alpha = 1$ for spherical particles.

TABLE 5-1

Rate of Fall in Water at 25°C for Particles Having a Specific Gravity of 2

| Size (microns) | Approximate Distance (cm) Traveled Prior to Reaching Terminal Velocity | Approximate Terminal Velocity (cm./sec.) |
|---|---|---|
| 2000 | $1.2 \times 10^2$ | 240 |
| 200 | $1.2 \times 10^{-2}$ | 2.4 |
| 20 | $1.2 \times 10^{-6}$ | $2.4 \times 10^{-2}$ |
| 2 | $1.2 \times 10^{-10}$ | $2.4 \times 10^{-4}$ |
| 0.2 | $1.2 \times 10^{-14}$ | $2.4 \times 10^{-6}$ |
| 0.02 | $1.2 \times 10^{-18}$ | $2.4 \times 10^{-8}$ |

### Sedimentation in a Centrifugal Field

When the particle size is smaller than 2 microns, settling times under a gravitational force become extremely long (see Table 5-1), apart from the complications due to Brownian motion, so that sedimentation in a centrifugal field must be employed.

After attainment of terminal velocity, equations 3, 7, and 9 can be combined to give

$$v = \frac{\alpha M^2(\rho_1 - \rho_2)w^2 R}{18\eta} \tag{12}$$

Nevertheless, since

$$v = \frac{dR}{dt} \tag{13}$$

integration between limits yields

$$t = t_2 - t_1 = \frac{18\eta \ln \dfrac{R_2}{R_1}}{\alpha M^2(\rho_1 - \rho_2)w^2} \tag{14}$$

where the subscripts 1 and 2 refer to the initial and final conditions respectively, so that $R_1$ and $R_2$ are the distances of the particle from the center of rotation before and after centrifugation.

## PREPARATION OF SUSPENSION FOR SEDIMENTATION

As with other particle size measurement techniques, the proper dispersion of particulate matter into the working units is imperative. Therefore criteria for choosing a sedimentation fluid and techniques for dispersing and testing for proper dispersion are discussed next.

### Choice of Sedimentation Fluid

The decision to use a specific sedimentation fluid should be primarily based on how well it disperses the particulate matter under study. Other requirements, however, should be considered, for obvious reasons.

The particulate matter should be highly insoluble in the sedimentation fluid and must not react chemically with it. The viscosity and density of the sedimentation fluid must be so related to the density of particulate matter that a reasonable rate of fall is obtained during sedimentation, and so that a major portion, if not all, of the settling takes place in the region restricted by turbulent flow (equation 5) and Brownian motion (equation 6). Thus a viscous fluid raises both the upper and lower limits of validity for Stokes' law (equations 5 and 6). Care should be taken, however, when using highly viscous fluids, to assure removal of air bubbles. Other desirable properties of the sedimentation fluid are nontoxicity, availability, and low cost.

Often pure liquids or mixtures of liquids are unsatisfactory as sedimentation fluids, and dispersing agents have to be employed. These dispersing agents usually lower the surface tension of the liquid and, therefore, enhance the wettability of the surface of the particles. Table 5-2 is a tabulation of several dispersing agents that have been found helpful. Since the concentration of dispersing agents never exceeds

0.1%, corrections for density and viscosity of the liquids are usually unwarranted.

Table 5-3 lists sedimentation fluids that have been found satisfactory by various investigators. Some fluids are pure liquids; others contain

TABLE 5-2

Some Liquid Dispersing and Wetting Agents
(Useful Concentration Range 0.01–0.1%)

| Type of Liquid | Dispersing or Wetting Agent[a] | Supplier |
| --- | --- | --- |
| Water | Sterox® <br> Tetrasodium pyrophosphate <br> Sodium tripolyphosphate <br> Sodium hexametaphosphate <br> Santomerse® | Monsanto Chemical Co. <br> St. Louis 66, Mo. |
| | Triton X-100® <br> Tamol L or N® | Rohm and Haas Co. <br> Washington Square <br> Philadelphia 5, Pa. |
| | Nacconol NRSF® | National Aniline Div., <br> Allied Chem. & Dye Corp. <br> New York 6, N. Y. |
| | Daxad No. 23® | Dewey and Almy Chem. Co., <br> Cambridge 40, Mass. |
| | Tween 80® | Atlas Powder Co. <br> Wilmington 99, Del. |
| | Maraperse C, CB, or N® | Marathon Corp. <br> Rothschild, Wis. |
| | Soap (sodium stearate or <br> oleate) | Several sources available |
| | Sodium silicate | Several sources available |
| Organic liquid | Nacconol NRSF® | Given above |
| | Aerosol OT® | American Cyanamid Co. <br> 30 Rockefeller Plaza <br> New York 20, N. Y. |
| Heavy oil | Aerosol OT® | Given above |
| | Twitchell Base 8240® | Emery Industries <br> 4300 Carew Tower <br> Cincinnati 2, Ohio |
| Air | Tricalcium phosphate <br> Santocel® | Monsanto Chemical Co. <br> St. Louis 66, Mo. |

[a] ® indicates registered trademark of corresponding supplier.

TABLE 5-3

Sedimentation Fluids for Powders[a]

| Powder | Liquid | Dispersing Agent and Weight Concentration |
|---|---|---|
| Alumina | Carbon tetrachloride | |
| Barium carbonate | Methanol | |
| Bronze powder | Cyclohexanol | |
| Calcium carbonate | Water | 0.1% Tetrasodium pyro-phosphate |
| Calcium arsenate | 1:1 Mixture of ethanol and water | |
| Calcium phosphate (soluble) | Isobutanol Hexane 2-Ethyl hexanol | |
| Calcium phosphate (insoluble) | Ethanol (absolute) Butanol Water | 0.1% $Na_3SiO_3$ and 0.02% Sterox® |
| | Water | 0.1% Sodium hexameta-phosphate |
| Cement | Glycol Paraffin oil Ethanol | 0.5% $CaCl_2$ |
| Clay | Water | 0.1% Sodium hexameta-phosphate |
| Coal | Ethanol | |
| Copper powder | Acetone Water | |
| Diatomaceous Earth | Water | 0.1% Sodium hexameta-phosphate |
| Fluorspar | Water | 0.02% Nitric acid |
| Glass particles | Butanol | |
| Graphite powder | Water Ethanol | 0.05% Tannic acid |
| Gypsum | Glycol | Cobalt citrate |
| Iron metal | 1:1 Volume mixture of ace-tone and soya bean oil Water | |
| Organic powders (cocoa, flour, starch, etc.) | Benzene Isobutanol | |
| Silica | Water | 0.1% Tetrasodium pyro-phosphate and 0.02% Sterox® |
| Sodium phosphates | Ethanol (absolute) | |
| Tungsten metal | Water Methanol Acetone | |
| Zinc metal | Butanol | |

[a] For many powders more than one dispersing agent may be satisfactory.

one or more dispersing agents. The use of dispersing agents is obviously governed by the goodness of the dispersion. But the initial choice of a sedimentation fluid still remains a trial-and-error process.

When a gas, for example, air, is used as the sedimentation fluid, the addition of about 1% tricalcium phosphate or finely divided silica to the powder may significantly improve the flow properties of the mixture (16) and hence enhance ease of dispersability.

### Dispersion Techniques

When a gas is used as the sedimentation medium, the powder can be dispersed by blowing it through an orifice and/or by letting it pass through a vibrating sieve.

The degree of dispersion achieved by a dispersion technique must be such that the material is broken up into the particulate units of interest. There are four major techniques for liquid dispersion. The first technique is to weigh the powder into a flask, introduce the fluid, and then shake it by hand vigorously for a few minutes. The second technique is to utilize stirring motors to achieve the dispersion. A convenient homogenizer which does not allow liquid vapors to reach the electric motor is merchandized by Fisher Scientific Co. under the trade name of Vir Tis Homogenizer.

The third dispersion technique, which should be only utilized for nonfragile particles, for example, powdered metals, is to place fractions of a gram of the powder on the larger of two lapped carbide blocks. The smaller block is then placed on top of the powder. The powder is ground for 20 seconds by applying a firm pressure to the top block while moving it in a circle. The powder is then brushed and washed with the sedimentation fluid into a vessel. After the suspension is made to volume, a few seconds of hand shaking is desirable.

The fourth liquid dispersion technique is spatulation. Here the desired weight of powder is placed on a flat surface, for example, a glass plate, a few drops of the liquid fluid are added, and the powder is worked for 2–10 minutes, as required, with a flexible-blade metal spatula. A fairly heavy pressure and a circular motion are used, with more liquid being added occasionally to keep the thick suspension moist during spatulation. The powder is then washed into a flask containing the appropriate amount of fluid and made into the final suspension by shaking for a few seconds.

Michaels et al. (17, 18) have made the only comprehensive study on the effect of dispersion techniques on the measured particle size distribution. Their results on tungsten powder dispersions in water show that hand shaking is the least effective dispersion technique, whereas spatulation produced the finest dispersion. The other techniques gave dispersions of intermediate fineness.

## Tests for Proper Dispersion

Tests for proper dispersion are important because they are useful in deciding on the technique of dispersion, the sedimentation fluid, and the concentration of dispersing agent (if any is needed). Several criteria for assessing the degree of dispersion have been described (19, 20) in the literature, and they depend on the difference in colloidal properties between deflocculated and flocculated suspensions.

Critical microscopic examination is the simplest way to determine the degree of dispersion. A drop of the dilute suspension is placed on a microscope slide and then covered with a cover glass to slow down evaporation. A well-dispersed suspension will show evenly spaced particles that do not stick to one another as they move within the fluid. A flocculated suspension will show an irregular structure in which the individual particles can be easily recognized. For particles with a size greater than 30 microns, microscopic examination is not very helpful because only a small field can be observed and particle movement is absent.

The study of the rheological behavior of high concentrations of powder in a fluid is useful in determining the degree of deflocculation. For example, approximately 50% slurry of kaolin in water acts as a solid mass, has a yield point, and exhibits dilatant behavior (21), whereas the addition of a few tenths of a percent of polyphosphates causes the mass to flow like a soup. The consistency of the paste can be observed by working with a spatula, with the better dispersing fluid giving a suspension that has a lower apparent viscosity. The rheological test is very useful for the preliminary choice of dispersing medium and agent. Phelps and Maguire (22) utilized it to choose a deflocculating agent for clay in water. The fluidity-electrolyte curves for 50% solids clay showed that sodium hexametaphosphate was a better deflocculating agent than sodium silicate or organic electrolytes.

Another test for determining the optimum level of addition of a dispersing agent is to measure sediment volume in about 5% slurry, after it has stood for a convenient period depending on the particle size range. A minimum sediment volume indicates the best level of concentration of a dispersing agent, and if several dispersing agents are compared, the best additive. It is important that the settling should not be disturbed mechanically or by heat convection currents.

Making actual sedimentation runs is also helpful. As the degree of dispersion increases, the percent of fines increases. This technique was utilized by Maguire and Phelps (22) for clay-water dispersions and by Vandersall and Irani (23) for insoluble calcium phosphate-water dispersions in choosing a dispersing agent and its level of addition. Michaels (17) found that as the dielectric constant of the liquid increased, it became a better dispersant for tungsten metal, with water giving the finest and benzene the coarsest dispersion.

### Particle Concentration

Care should be taken in choosing the particle concentration for a sedimentation experiment. Theoretically, the concentration should be low enough (about 0.05%) that every particle has sufficient space to settle independently, but high enough that it can be accurately detected. In most cases these two restrictions cannot be met simultaneously, and a compromise must be made. In general, a volume concentration of around 0.2–0.5% gives acceptable results.

### Physical Constants for Sedimentation

When making use of Stokes' equation in particle size distribution measurements, we must know the particle density and the viscosity and density of the fluid. The particle density can be determined pycnometrically (24), and preferably  in the sedimentation fluid itself. By so doing an accurate difference in density between the particle and sedimentation fluid is obtained even if the particle has internal pores that are not wetted by the fluid. The usual procedure is to measure the volume of a pycnometer, for example, 10 cc, with a suitable fluid whose density is known. About 1 gm of powder is accurately weighed into the pycnometer, equilibrated in a temperature bath while air is pumped out of the sample with a vacuum pump or a water aspirator. Deaerated fluid is then introduced into the pycnometer and the slurry is temperature equilibrated. The particle density is calculated by dividing the weight of powder by the volume of fluid it displaced.

The density of the fluid at any temperature can be measured by a straightforward pycnometric (24) technique, and the viscosities can be measured with an Ostwald-type viscosimeter. Table 5-4 is a tabulation of densities and viscosities of fluids commonly employed in sedimentation. Data on other fluids are available in handbooks (25).

The value of the acceleration due to gravity is 981 cm/sec$^2$ at sea level and is slightly dependent on the altitude and position on earth (25$a$). The range, however, is only 979–981 cm/sec$^2$ for most locations.

TABLE 5-4

Physical Constants of Some Sedimentation Fluids at 25°C

| Fluid | Density (gm/cc) | Viscosity (centipoise) |
|---|---|---|
| Air | $(1.19 \times 10^{-3})^a$ | $(1.9 \times 10^{-4})^a$ |
| Acetone | 0.790 | 0.316 |
| Benzene | 0.87 | 0.61 |
| Butanol | 0.81 | 2.62 |
| Carbon tetrachloride | 1.582 | 0.919 |
| Ethanol | 0.78 | 1.10 |
| 2-Ethyl hexanol | 0.83 | 7.5 |
| Glycerin | 1.26 | 954 |
| Hexane | 0.66 | 0.294 |
| Isobutanol | 0.80 | 3.3 |
| Methanol | 0.79 | 0.547 |
| Propanol | 0.81 | 2.00 |
| Toluene | 0.86 | 0.56 |
| Water | 0.997 | 0.894 |

[a] At a pressure of 76 cm of mercury.

## GRAVITATIONAL TECHNIQUES BASED ON CHANGE IN CONCENTRATION AT A GIVEN LEVEL

This technique consists of measuring the concentration versus time of particles at a given distance $h$ below the surface of an initially homogeneous suspension. The particle size distribution function $f(M)$, previously elucidated in Chapter 4, is

$$f(M) = \frac{d(c/c_0)}{dM} \tag{15}$$

where $c_0$ is the total concentration and $c$ is the concentration of particles with a size between $M$ and $M + dM$, so that $d(c/c_0)$ is the fraction of particles with a size between $M$ and $M + dM$.

At the end of any given time $t$ and at a distance $h$ below the surface, the concentration will have decreased by an amount equal to the concentration of particles in the initial suspension which were sufficiently large to have settled the distance $h$ in time $t$. Smaller particles will have settled from the sampling position during this time, but they will have been replaced by other particles from higher levels. Therefore the concentration $c_t$ at time $t$ is

$$\frac{c_t}{c_0} = \int_0^{M_t} f(M)\, dM = \text{fraction finer than } M_t \tag{16}$$

where $M_t$ is defined by equation 11 at the particular time of sampling.

Before discussing the particular methods that employ the technique of change in concentration at a given level, we mention the general advantages and disadvantages. The obvious advantage of these techniques is that particle size distributions are directly obtained from the data without requiring any mathematical calculations except for simple division and use of Stokes' equation. On the other hand, the techniques are particularly sensitive to convection currents inasmuch as changes in local concentration are always attributed to sedimentation. In addition, since the simple version of Stokes' equation requires a fairly dilute suspension, a thick horizontal plane is normally sampled instead of the assumed and hypothetical infinitesimal layer. Moreover, in most cases the measuring devices disturb the sedimentation column and in some cases seriously affect the normal settling of the suspension.

### Andreasen Pipet Method

In the 1930's Andreasen and coworkers (26, 27) described a simple method for particle size distribution measurements. The method employs relatively simple apparatus. In a run, small samples of suspension are pipetted during sedimentation at a specific depth and the concentration of particulate matter is determined either analytically or by evaporating an aliquot to dryness and weighing the resulting solid. Each sample drawn has a smaller particle size than that corresponding to the falling velocity given by Stokes' law because all particles of larger size will have fallen below the level of the pipet tip.

The pipet method has been widely used and subjected to modification (28) because the operation is so simple and its hardware is so inexpensive (Fisher Scientific Co. sells a kit for around $30).

Even though the pipet method offers the advantages we have listed, it involves an inherent error that makes the results somewhat unreliable. The continuous removal of sample from the suspension considerably disturbs the sedimentation medium and falsifies one of the assumptions made in Stokes' equation, namely, that sedimentation is proceeding under steady-state conditions. In addition, since dilute (around 0.5%) concentrations must be employed in sedimentation techniques, a relatively large sample must normally be removed to determine the particulate concentration accurately. Such removal causes a change in sedimentation height which should be corrected for.

Hinkley (29) suggested that the concentration of particulate matter be determined by using a specific gravity bottle in order to "save a good deal of time and effort." The change of specific gravity with sedimentation, however, is normally so slight that Hinkley's modification causes the results to be more unreliable in certain cases.

Berg's (30) variation of Andreasen's method is to remove the sample from a side arm fastened permanently near the bottom of the sedimentation column.

## The Diver Method

This method was first developed by Berg (30–32). The method makes use of small glass divers of known density that are inserted into the suspension and that settle at the level at which the density is equal to that of the diver. They continue to sink at this density level as sedimentation progresses. Each diver contains a metallic or heavy strip and is weighted to the required density with alcohol. A number of divers is required since each diver gives only one point on the size distribution curve. The divers are small and no stem breaks the surface during a run, so that errors due to surface tension are eliminated. By using globular divers having a diameter of about 7 mm, measurements can be made at very small depths from the surface of the suspension, so that particles as small as 0.2 micron can be measured.

In the diver method, it is assumed that particulate concentration is proportional to the difference in density between the suspension and the pure fluid, as measured by the position of the divers. Because divers of diameters less than 2 cm have been exclusively used, the uncertainty in height measurement is relatively small. In addition, since the divers travel with the medium, deposition on the divers is minimized.

The major disadvantage to Berg's diver method is that the divers are not usually visible in the suspension because they are small, so that they have to be located by attracting them to the well of the glass sedimentation tube by means of a magnet, thus disturbing steady-state sedimentation. Jarrett et al. (33) minimized this disturbance by employing as a detector for the divers an alternating-current inductance-resistance bridge; the high permeability Permalloy strip in the diver destroyed the balance in the bridge when a thin search coil surrounding the sedimentation column was moved past the diver.

The other disadvantage to the diver method is the complicated wall-effect corrections that have to be used (34), as discussed by Berg (32).

## Hydrometer Method

This technique was developed by several investigators (33, 35, 36) because of simplicity of operation and low cost of hardware. It is assumed that the difference in density between the suspension and pure fluid as measured with a hydrometer is proportional to the concentration. The major problem is to decide at what position on the hydrometer the concentration of particulate matter corresponds to the hydometer reading. The position of this level is somewhat indeterminate, and since the hydrometer sinks as sedimentation proceeds, the position is not constant.

Other disadvantages of the hydrometer method are the deposition of material on the hydrometer and/or the disturbance of steady-state settling when the hydrometer is inserted and removed from the suspension. Moreover, since part of the hydrometer is in the air, surface tension corrections should be applied for more absolute results.

A detailed description of the hydrometer technique together with nomographs that interrelate specific gravities, temperature, time, size, and viscosity of the medium is presented by Lester (37). Lester's detailed method is directly adaptable to quality control laboratories. Sammarone and Saunders (38) utilized a modified hydrometer method to measure the particle size distribution of milled enamels and color oxides. Their modification, which does not eliminate inherent errors in the hydrometer method, is to use a Westphall balance to measure the specific gravity.

For determining particle size distributions Weaver (39) described an automatic hydrometer method whereby the weight which counterbalances a metal bob in the suspension increases continuously as sedimentation proceeds. Using a motor-driven chainomatic balance, the weight is added, and the weight imbalance is detected by a differential transformer which is amplified and recorded simultaneously with the feeding of the motor. The cumulative weight additions, as they appear on the recorder chart, are then interpreted to determine the particle size distribution.

Several authors (40) describe specific adaptations of the hydrometer method. Technical associations have also published detailed descriptions of hydrometer methods for particle size determination of clay minerals. Of these, the most complete are those of the Technical Association of the Pulp and Paper Industry (41) and the ASTM (42). The first deals specifically with paper clays and makes use of a nomograph for solution of Stokes' law. The ASTM procedure is designed for the analysis of soils, but contains tabular data that make preparation of calculation charts easier.

Specifically, the hydrometer determines the density of the suspension near the hydrometer's geometric center. Since the hydrometer changes the height of the sedimentation column, the effective sedimentation height $h$ is

$$h = h_1 + \frac{1}{2}\left(h_2 - \frac{V_b}{A}\right) \tag{17}$$

where $h_1$ is the distance from the top of the hydrometer bulb to the surface of the suspension, $h_2$ is the length of the hydrometer bulb, $V_b$ is the volume of the bulb, and $A$ is the cross-sectional area of the sedimentation vessel. The weight of particulate matter per milliliter of suspension, $W$, is

$$W = \frac{\rho_1(\rho_3 - \rho_2)}{(\rho_1 - \rho_2)} \tag{18}$$

where $\rho_1$, $\rho_2$, and $\rho_3$ are the densities of the particle, pure fluid, and suspension respectively, with $\rho_3$ being determined from the hydrometer reading. In addition,

$$\text{fraction finer than } M_t = \frac{\rho_1(\rho_3 - \rho_2)}{W_0(\rho_1 - \rho_2)} \tag{19}$$

where $W_0$ is the weight of particulate matter per milliliter of suspension at time zero, and $M_t$ is the size computed for the time at which $\rho_3$ was measured. As mentioned before, tables and nomographs can be constructed to facilitate the computations. Care must be taken that the correct density and viscosity are used if experiments are done at different temperatures.

## Manometer Method

The manometer method of analysis takes either of two different forms. In the first, the apparatus (43) consists of a vertical-side tube containing pure fluid from which the suspension was prepared, connected to the sedimentation vessel at a known distance beneath the surface of the suspension. The pure fluid column has a greater height than that of the suspension because of its lower density. Measurement of this excess height at various times gives the variations of the mean density of the suspension between the surface of the suspension and the sampling level. The method suffers the disadvantage that the change of excess height with time is small, so that accurate measurement is difficult if not impossible. In addition, the raw data have to be differentiated twice before the particle size frequency curve is obtained; the difficulties associated with differentiation are well known.

Another problem is that the manometer tends to be sluggish in action and the fluid in the manometer can become contaminated with powder that has migrated from the sedimentation vessel.

The second procedure is to use differential manometers (33), with the advantage that the mean density of a thin slab of suspension is measured, eliminating one differentiation step of the data treatment. Nevertheless, the difficulties arising from the sluggishness and contamination of the manometer are not eliminated.

## Activation Analysis Method

The activation analysis method uses the activity induced in the particles by neutron bombardment to measure the weight of material in suspension. During irradiation the activity induced in a particle is proportional to the number of atoms in the particle. Consequently, the relative activity between two particles is equal to their relative weights. Similarly, in a lamina of a settling suspension the relative activity at any time is proportional to the weight concentration of particles in the lamina.

Abraham et al. (44) used the gravitational activation analysis method to measure the particle size distribution of powdered uranium dioxide. They measured the activity with a scintillation counter versus time at a fixed distance from the top of the suspension through a collimating slit positioned in a lead shield. The ratio of activity at any time to the initial activity yields the cumulative undersize weight distribution.

Sources of error peculiar to the activation analysis method which must be partly corrected for are counting statistics and scattered radiation. The counting statistics actually limit the accuracy of the method for the finer part of the size distribution, with the largest weight fractions being known with the greatest precision. Another obvious limitation of this technique is that a neutron source should be available and the material itself should have an isotope with a relatively long half-life so that no decay corrections become necessary. Special handling and disposal of isotopes are other complications to be considered.

Abraham et al. (44) have also suggested that through discrimination of the respective radiations the determination of the particle size distribution of the components in a mixture can become feasible without the necessity of separating the powder into its components. Bate and Leddicote (45) utilized this idea to determine the particle size distribution of mixtures of thorium and uranium oxides and of mixtures of oxides of iron, chromium, zirconium, and uranium.

## Photometric Method

Richardson (46) developed and Rose (7) refined the photometric method. In the apparatus, a parallel beam of light, of a vertical depth that is small compared to the distance of the beam below the surface of the suspension, is projected across the suspension onto a photoelectric cell. Readings of the emergent light intensity are then taken at known times while the powder settles out of the suspension under the influence of gravity.

The photometric method requires the use of the Beer-Lambert equation

$$I = I_0 \exp\left(\frac{-Kcl}{M}\right) \tag{20}$$

where $M$ is the size of the particle, $I_0$ is the intensity of light in the absence of particulate matter, $I$ is the intensity of light after passing through the suspension, $c$ is the weight concentration of particles, $l$ is the length of the light path in the suspension, and $K$ is a constant.

Equation 20 specifies that log $(I_0/I)$ is directly proportional to the length of the light path and particulate concentration. This assumption becomes unrealistic as the particle size decreases because of diffraction and interference effects. If the photocell, however, subtends a very small solid angle at the center of the suspension (7), the light-scattering and diffraction complications are minimized. An instrument with a photocell subtending a solid angle of $2.2 \times 10^{-4}$ radians and employing Rose's photometric sedimentation method has recently been commercialized (7, 47).

Since the value of $K$ is generally unknown, equation 20 is written in the form

$$\ln \frac{I_0}{I} = Acl \tag{21}$$

where $A$ is the projected area per gram of particles and $Ac$ is the projected area per unit volume. Therefore, the plot of the ratio $(\ln I_0/I_t)/(\ln I_0/I)$ versus the values of size as computed from Stokes' equation for time $t$ gives the cumulative undersize distribution by area, where $I_t$ is the intensity of transmitted light at time $t$. Rose (7) also showed that the cumulative undersize by weight can be evaluated by integrating the area under the absorbance, $\ln I_0/I$, versus size curve.

One advantage of the photometric method is that the size distribution is obtainable by integrating rather than differentiating experimental data, which is more precise. In addition, a recording automatic apparatus may be constructed, as was done by Talvite and Paulus (48). These authors also continuously lowered the sedimentation vessel with a synchronous motor, while keeping the light source and photoelectric cell stationary, in order to allow large particles to sediment a larger distance than small particles, prior to being detected.

The major difficulty with the photometric method is that equations 20 and 21 are based on the assumption that the light cut off by a particle is equal to its projected area, immaterial of its size or chemical composition. This assumption is often unjustified, and it is necessary that the relation between the absorbance and particulate concentration be known for each powder over a wide range of particle size prior to making a run on an unknown sample. This makes the method particularly undesirable as a research tool.

Other inherent and questionable assumptions are that all particles are absolutely opaque, that there is no reflection between the particles or between the particles and the walls of the sedimentation vessel, and that the concentration of the suspension is low enough that no two particles fall on the same line parallel to the light beam.

Brown and Skrebowski (49) briefly described at a particle size symposium a method for measuring particle concentration in suspensions using X-ray activation. They split an X-ray beam into two parts, one being the reference beam falling on a fluorescent screen, the second beam passing through a sedimentation cell onto a second fluorescent screen. They found that if $I_0$ is the intensity of the X-ray beam when passing through a cell containing pure liquid and $I$ the intensity of the X-ray beam when passing through the same cell containing the liquid with $A$ gm of material in suspension, then $\log (I_0/I) = KA$, where $K$ is a constant. The method is only suitable for chemically homogeneous materials because the absorption coefficient $K$ is dependent on chemical composition.

## GRAVITATIONAL CUMULATIVE TECHNIQUES

The basic principle for cumulative sedimentation techniques is to measure the amount of particulate matter that settles at a specific distance below the surface of the suspension versus time. At the beginning of the sedimentation experiment the particulate matter can be either homogeneously distributed or concentrated in another layer of suspension on top of the actual sedimentation fluid.

### Layer Methods

If particulate matter is initially concentrated in a layer whose thickness is small compared to the distance below the surface at which the amount settled is measured, then particle size distributions can be directly obtained through the use of Stokes' equation and a simple calculation of the ratio of the amount settled at any time to the total weight of the sample. Marshall (50) was the first to utilize this layer principle. Although the layer method is intuitively simple and straightforward, no completely adequate apparatus has been yet developed.

Eadie and Payne developed a commercial (51) instrument called the Micromerograph which utilizes the layer sedimentation principle in air. In the device a sample of powder is placed in a recessed holder and blasted with compressed gas through a narrow slit into the sedimentation chamber which is about $7\frac{1}{2}$ feet long and 4 inches in diameter. The particles sediment on a pan of an electronic balance located at the bottom of the column so that the cumulative weight is automatically recorded as a function of time. The cumulative weight-time curve is then converted to a particle size distribution using charts having $M$, $\rho_1$, and time as variables, where $\rho_1$ is the particle density. Although the charts supplied with the Micromerograph are supposed to be corrected for deviations from Stokes' law and variations in initial velocity, several complications peculiar to sedimentation in gases, for example, air, are not eliminated.

Although the advantage of obtaining the results speedily is obvious, uncertainties in air sedimentation are usually serious. No check can be made of whether proper dispersion of the particles was attained, and in many cases it is not achieved. It is also well known (52) that particles acquire a high surface charge during motion in air, and indeed, in extreme cases, 30% of finely divided phosphates during a Micromerograph determination stuck (53) on the walls of the sedimentation vessel. Since surface charge is dependent on the relative humidity in the room, chemical composition, and particular size of the particle, a nonrepresentative sample often reaches the bottom of the sedimentation column for measurement. As was pointed out earlier, the limits of Stokes' equation are also significantly narrowed because of slippage (6) caused by the large mean free path for gaseous molecules. Finally, large eddy currents resulting from the mixing of the suspension with the air below it can distort the size distribution. All these errors make the claim (50) of an accuracy of $\pm 3\%$ throughout the size range of 1–250 microns highly questionable, particularly if it is borne in mind that the Reynolds number for particles over 50 microns settling in air is often larger than 1.0.

The Werner (54), Palo-Myers (55), and Travis (56) methods also operate on the layer technique, but utilize a liquid suspension on top of a column of clear liquid. Several objections to these crude apparatus can be listed, with the most important being the effect of eddy currents (density streaming) that causes particles in the suspension to settle through mixing, aside from normal sedimentation. Other objections are the absence of temperature control, which intensifies eddy currents, and the sticking of particles to the walls of the entrance to the measuring device, which has a smaller diameter than the sedimentation vessel. In these methods, the amount settled is determined by measuring the height of the sediment, so that we readily obtain a particle size distribution based on bulk density. Since bulk density, or settled volume, is not independent of particle size itself, the results can be questionable if no corrections are made. Moreover, since particles tend to diffuse back up after settling to the bottom, the reading of settled height includes an estimation.

Whitby (57) eliminated two major complications from the layer technique. By using a feeding suspension (the layer) that has a lower density but a higher viscosity than the clear sedimentation liquid, the adverse effect of density streaming is minimized, and all particles do start from the same point. Whitby also utilized a streamlined sedimentation tube and a tapper to minimize particle sticking to the entrance of the capillary at the bottom of the sedimentation tube. Whitby's technique is discussed further and in more detail in the section on centrifugal layer methods.

### Homogeneous Suspension

The principle of this method involves measurement of the over-all concentration change in a suspension as a function of time. The over-all concentration has been measured with manometers or by difference, using a balance situated at the bottom of the sedimentation vessel that weighs the settled particulate matter.

As discussed previously, manometric methods are suspect because it is difficult to measure accurately the small pressures produced by low concentration and partly because the return of clear liquid from a side arm causes convection in the suspension. The sedimentation balance, on the other hand, is free from these defects. As a result of the great sensitivity of the sedimentation balance method a very low concentration may be used. The only factor that could cause interference with the settling is the movement of the balance pan, and this can be minimized greatly by proper choice of balance. A further advantage is that it is unnecessary to know the initial concentration.

When the sedimentation of particles initially in a homogeneous suspension takes place, the weight settled consists of (1) those particles whose time of fall is less than the time specified, and whose size therefore is greater than that defined by Stokes' equation for the specific time of fall, and (2) those particles whose time of fall for the suspension height $h$ is longer than the time specified, but which have settled because of their intermediate position in the fluid column. A method to separate the total weight settled into these two components is as follows, based on methods first developed by Oden (58) and later modified by others (59–63).

The fraction of particles lying in the size between $M$ and $M + dM$ is $f(M)\ dM$, where $f(M)$ is the frequency of occurrence of size $M$. The total weight settled, $W$, at time $t$ is made up of two fractions, one of particles greater than and the other less than a given size:

$$W = \int_{M_1}^{M_{\max}} f(M)\ dM + \int_{M_{\min}}^{M_1} \frac{vt}{h} f(M)\ dM \tag{22}$$

where $M_1$ is the size of those particles which would just fall the full distance $h$ in time $t$, $v$ the velocity of fall for a particle with size $M$ (less than $M_1$), and $h$ the height of the suspension. The sizes $M_{\min}$ and and $M_{\max}$ are the smallest and largest sizes of the distribution respectively. Differentiating equation 22 with respect to time,

$$\frac{dW}{dt} = \int_{M_{\min}}^{M_1} \frac{vt}{h} f(M)\ dM \tag{23}$$

or

$$t\frac{dW}{dt} = \int_{M_{\min}}^{M_1} \frac{vt}{h} f(M)\ dM \tag{24}$$

Combining equations 22 and 24,

$$W = \int_{M_1}^{M_{\max}} f(M)\ dM + t\frac{dW}{dt} \tag{25}$$

Therefore:

$$w = \int_{M_1}^{M_{\max}} f(M)\ dM = W - t\frac{dW}{dt} \tag{26}$$

where $w$ is the weight fraction of particles with a size $M_1$ or larger. Therefore, $w$ can be evaluated by plotting $W$ against $t$ and drawing tangents to the curve at different values of $t$, as shown in Fig. 5-1, with the intercept on the $W$ axis being equal to $w$ for that particular time. The accuracy with which the tangents can be drawn is low, however, particularly at low values of $t$. It is preferable to use the procedure proposed by Gaudin et al. (61), who wrote equation 26 as

$$w = W - \frac{dW}{d \ln t} \tag{27}$$

and plotted $W$ versus $\ln t$. Evaluation of $w$ is then carried out by plotting values of $W$ and $dW/d \ln t$ on the same scale and measuring the difference of the two abscissas at that specific time, as illustrated in Fig. 5-2. The determination of $w$, as given in Fig. 5-2, can be highly faciltated (64) using a special protractor to evaluate $dW/d \ln t$ and an expandable ruler to measure the ratio $[W - (dw/d \ln t)]/W$,

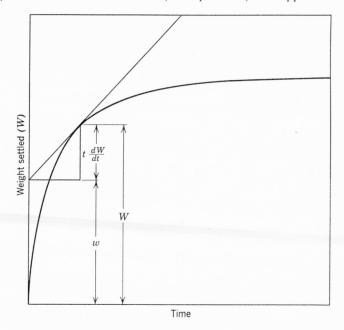

FIG. 5-1. Interpretation of cumulative sedimentation technique for an initially homogeneous suspension.

which is the fraction of particles larger than the size determined by Stokes' equation 11 for the specific time of measurement. This procedure is discussed further in Chapter 10.

Jarrett and Heywood (33) and Nissan (65) criticized cumulative methods because of the need for differentiation, on the grounds that slight discontinuities in the frequency distribution curve cannot be detected. Donoghue (66), however, has shown from a detailed and excellent study that the claimed complications are baseless, particularly if the fraction deposited is determined at times increasing by a factor of not more than $\sqrt{2}$, a restriction obviously met by automatic sedimentation balances.

Since sedimentation balances are capable of giving particle size distributions with a high degree of accuracy, several reliable apparatus have been constructed and investigated. Some of these apparatus are described later. When balance pans are utilized, the materials of construction should not, obviously, react with the sedimentation fluid.

The use of an anlytical balance, whereby small counter weights were automatically added as sedimentation proceeded, for weighing particles

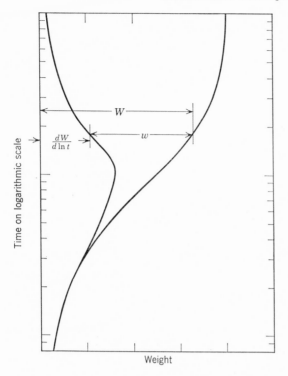

FIG. 5-2. Interpretation of cumulative sedimentation techniques for an initially homogeneous suspension from a logarithmic plot.

settling out of a suspension was first described by Oden (58, 67), Svedberg and Rinde (68) described the first recording automatic sedimentation balance. Their method, with an accuracy of $10^{-4}$ gm, utilized a contact to sense the inbalance caused by particles settling on a balance pan. The compensation for the weight inbalance, caused by the increasing weight of sediment, was accomplished by means of an electric current that caused a small motor to pull the other arm of the balance. The time-current plot was automatically recorded and later converted to a time-weight relation. Bishop (69) described another recording sedimentation balance, whereas Edwald (63) recorded the change in pressure on the wall of the sedimentation vessel as sedimentation proceeded, and assumed it to be proportional to the amount of particulate matter settled. Lohmann (70) described an electric recording balance suitable for conversion to a sedimentation balance. As with the other apparatus mentioned, however, complicated servomechanism balancing circuits were required.

Rabatin and Gale (7) described a simple recording sedimentation balance. They utilized a sensitive spring to weigh the particles settled on the pan. As the weight on the pan increased, a shutter mechanism directly attached to the spring intercepted a parallel light that was focused on a photocell, with the change in photocell current being automatically recorded. One difficulty with this method is that the spring ages with time, so that the spring constant must be determined occasionally.

Bachmann and Gerstenberg (72) evaluated a commercial recording sedimentation balance, called Recording Sedibal (73), and found it to give more precise results than the Andreasen pipet method. The mode of operation of this balance is as follows. As soon as a 2-mg weight of sediment has deposited in the pan, the normal position of a beam is altered, causing a ray of light to operate a photoelectric system which actuates a step-by-step motor by means of a relay. This motor twists a torsion wire through a given angle, with the resulting force transmitting a torsional moment to a secondary beam fixed to the torsion wire. The torsional force in this wire is in turn transmitted to the main beam by a mechanical coupling and turns it back to its original position, thereby automatically compensating for the load on the pan and at the same time cutting off the light beam to the photocell. This procedure is repeated until the whole sample is sedimented. Concurrent with this operation, a recording pen moves at each step of the motor, while vertically to this direction the chart paper of the recorder moves at a constant speed.

One complication with the Recording Sedibal, as with the other sedimentation balances we have described, is that the balance pan is immersed in the suspension, with the result that streaming of particles (59) around the pan may take place. Another source of error is that small convection currents may be caused by changes in suspension density directly under the pan as particles settle out. Bostock (62) designed a balance that eliminated these objections by having the balance pan immediately under and surrounding the bottom of the sedimentation vessel. A commercial instrument (74) based on Bostock's design is available. To take readings on it requires, however, the continuous attention of an operator.

Ames et al. (75) automatized the Gallenkamp balance by fastening the core of a linear variable differential transformer to the balance beam. The output of the transformer, which was found to be proportional to the weight sedimented on the pan, was amplified and recorded. They also utilized solenoid valves and a sequence switching arrangement to facilitate the operation of the balance. The total mantime required to obtain the raw data was reduced to about 5–10 minutes.

An imaginative use of the balance method was applied by Taylor and Harmon (76) to the measurement of drop sizes of water sprays. They utilized a balance whose pan was suspended in liquid hexane cooled to −20° C. When the water droplets impinged on the hexane surface, they quickly froze and then proceeded to settle through the hexane onto the balance pan. This technique seems to be promising in liquid spray research.

Ross (77) recently utilized the transmittance of X-rays from an Am²⁴¹ source at a fixed height to follow the rate of sedimentation of an initially homogeneous uranium oxide suspension.

### CENTRIFUGAL TECHNIQUES BASED ON CHANGE IN CONCENTRATION AT A GIVEN DEPTH

The technique is analogous to the Andreasen pipet method, so that all the errors previously described apply here. The major problem, however, is the precise determination of concentration as a function of time at a given depth below the surface of the suspension. Kamack (78) devised a sector-shaped centrifuge with a built-in pipet capable of removing samples during sedimentation in order to avoid errors caused by repeated stopping and starting of the centrifuge.

Although the operation of the instrument seems to be satisfactory, the calculations for particle size distributions are fairly complex; they involve evaluation of an indefinite integral whose value must be determined by the approximate trapezoidal integration technique.

Gupta (79) modified Kamack's method to avoid the complicated mathematical treatment of the results, by making the distance of sedimentation small compared to the radius of rotation. The liquid samples were withdrawn at a right angle to the plane of rotation with the acceleration being assumed constant over the distance of sedimentation. The reproducibility of the results for suspensions of dyestuff or polyvinyl chloride in the size range of 0.2–3 microns was excellent.

Berg (32) utilized his ingenious divers in centrifugal sedimentation also and claimed that particle size distributions in the range of 0.005–0.5 microns could be measured. The errors involved in the diver method, however, as previously discussed, plus the influence of diffusion and wall effects must be carefully considered.

## CENTRIFUGAL CUMULATIVE TECHNIQUES

### Layer Method

Marshall (50) was the first to utilize the layer technique; however, Whitby et al. (57, 80–82) were the first to describe a workable method. It has been commercialized (83) under the trade name M-S-A Particle Size Analyzer. Basic to the method are specially designed centrifuges that have speeds constant to within 1% and whose speed versus time curves during starting and stopping are known and constant enough that corrections do not vary by more than ±0.5 sec. Centrifuges of 300, 600, 1200, 1800, and 3600 RPM whose starting and stopping characteristics are controlled by a combination of an inertia disk and a variable resister in series with one winding of the motor have been

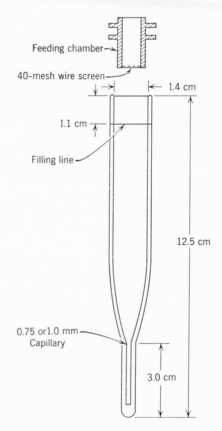

FIG. 5-3. Centrifuge tube and feeding chamber design according to Whitby (57, 80–82).

developed. Special centrifuge tubes and a feeding chamber are employed, as illustrated in Fig. 5-3.

At the beginning of a size analysis the clean tube is filled to the line near the top of the tube with a suitable sedimentation liquid. Next a suspension of particles is made up in a liquid that is miscible with the sedimentation liquid but has a slightly lower density and a slightly higher viscosity, in order to minimize density streaming. An aliquot of this suspension is placed in a feeding chamber (Fig. 5-3) and then transferred to the sedimentation tube, leaving a sharp layer of suspension on top of the sedimentation liquid. Then, at times calculated from Stokes' equation for desired sizes, the sediment height is read. When the particle size distribution lies below 20–30 microns, the sedimentation tube is transferred to the lowest-speed centrifuge and run for precalculated times, after which the sediment height is read. This is repeated using different times of centrifugation and the different centrifuges until no further change in sediment height is observed. The ratio of the sediment height at any time to the final height of sediment is assumed to give the fraction larger than the size calculated. With proper choice of sedimentation fluids, distribution of particle sizes in the range of 0.1–80 microns can be measured.

As we have mentioned, sediment height is assumed to be proportional to sediment weight. When complete dispersion of particulate matter is achieved, this is a good assumption, because one-size particles are essentially settling at one time, and the void space is independent of size for monodisperse systems. In many cases, however, strong aggregates of smaller particles exist, for example, 2-micron silica particles are aggregates of 0.01–0.03 ultimate particles. In these cases compression of the sediment column with increasing centrifuge speed takes place, and bulk density correction factors must be used (84).

Another complication with the M-S-A Particle Size Analyzer is that no temperature control is provided, so that data obtained in unairconditioned laboratories are suspect. When a material having a narrow size distribution is studied, many particles may enter the capillary at the same time, causing plugging. Although a tapper is provided to minimize plugging and surface diffusion after settling, it disturbs sedimentation. In some cases involving transparent particles, serious difficulty may arise in deciding where to read the sediment height, because a sharp line is not apparent.

## Homogeneous Suspension

The cumulative methods starting with an initially homogeneous suspension have been the most popular so far, although the layer techniques are certainly superseding them. The serious drawback in the use of a homogeneous suspension in a centrifuge is the complication involved in the calculation of results. This complication is due to the fact that the forces on any particle at any given time depend on its distance from center of rotation. The difficulty can be eliminated by making the radius of the centrifuge large compared to the sedimentation height, as was done by Menis et al. (85, 86), who utilized Oden's method (58–63) to interpret the cumulative weight data.

Equations for sector-shaped tubes were derived by Romwalter and Vendl (87) for the variable-time method, whereby the amount of material accumulated at different times is measured:

$$F = \int_0^M \frac{R^2}{R^2 - S^2} \left[ 1 - \exp \left\{ -\frac{2(\rho_1 - \rho_2)M^2w^2t}{18\eta} \right\} \right] f(M) \, dM$$

$$+ \int_M^\infty f(M) \, dM \quad (28)$$

where $F$ is the total weight fraction sedimented, $R$ the distance from center of rotation to bottom of suspension, $S$ the distance from center of rotation to surface of suspension, and $w$ the angular velocity in radians per second. An exact solution of equation 28 for the integral $\int_0^M f(M) \, dM$ has not been possible. Nevertheless, for sector-shaped tubes employing the variable height-of-sedimentation method, Brown (88) derived an exact solution:

$$\int_0^M f(M) \, dM = (1 - F) + \frac{R^2 - S^2}{2S} \frac{dF}{dS} \quad (29)$$

where $M$ is evaluated from equation 14 at $R_2 = R$ and $R_1 = S$.

If the centrifuge tubes are cylindrical in shape rather than sector-shaped and if errors caused by particles striking the sidewalls are neglected, equations 28 and 29 become (89):

$$F = \int_0^M \frac{R}{R - S} \left[ 1 - \exp \left\{ \frac{-2(\rho_1 - \rho_2)M^2w^2t}{18\eta} \right\} \right] f(M) \, dM$$

$$+ \int_M^\infty f(M) \, dM \quad (30)$$

for the variable-time method, and

$$\int_0^M f(M) \, dM = (1 - F) + (R - S) \frac{dF}{dS} \quad (31)$$

for the variable-height method.

As mentioned earlier, no exact solution for the centrifugal variable-time method has been found; rather, approximate solutions have been used. Jacobsen and Sullivan (90) described two such approximations. The first is to use a settling height that is small compared to the distance from the center of rotation to the bottom of the suspension, as was also done by Menis et al. (85, 86). Centrifugal sedimentation can be then regarded as equivalent to gravitational sedimentation, and equation 11 becomes

$$M = \left[ \frac{18\eta(R - S)}{t(\rho_1 - \rho_2)w^2\bar{r}} \right]^{1/2} \tag{32}$$

where $w^2\bar{r}$ is the average centrifugal acceleration and $t$ is the time corrected for starting and stopping the centrifuge (50). The other approximation, which is open to more serious questioning, is to neglect the errors caused by replacing the sector-shaped tubes with cylindrical tubes. In this method, the supernatant suspension at some level is separated from the sedimented material and the concentration $c_t$ determined to give the oversimplified equation

$$F = \frac{c_0 - c_t}{c_0} \tag{33}$$

Robison and Martin (91, 92) chose to solve equation 28 by successive approximation, but found that if $(R - S) \ll 1$ so that $R/S \simeq 1$, the solution becomes exact, yet complicated. Brown (87) utilized the variable-height method which has the advantage of being based on an exact solution for $\int_0^M f(M) \, dM$. Brown's method, however, is experimentally inconvenient (89) because the centrifugal force must be varied in order to determine the complete size distribution. Donoghue and Bostock (93) used a variation of Brown's method by employing a special centrifuge in which the distance from the center of rotation to the bottom of the suspension was varied.

The ultracentrifuge (94–96) can be utilized to measure particle size distributions in the submicron range, as first described by Svedberg. A popular commercial centrifuge is marketed by the Spinco Division of Beckman Instruments. The rotor of the centrifuge is spun at speeds of up to 60,000 RPM in a vacuum in order to minimize air drag.

Supercentrifuges have speeds that are intermediate between conventional and untracentrifuges. Saunders (97) published a nomograph for particle size determination with the Sharples' supercentrifuge, whereas Schachman (98) presented an extension and modification of previous theoretical work on the use of the supercentrifuge with very fine particles. A fractionated bentonite suspension was utilized to obtain a calibration factor for other substances.

Johnson (99) made an extensive investigation of centrifugal particle size distribution determination, as affected by wall effects, initial particle movement, centrifuge tube shape, limiting size for Stokes' equation, inclination of centrifuge tube, particle shape, and nonrandom errors such as unbalance in the centrifuge and acceleration and deceleration corrections. He concluded that none of these factors was large enough to affect the results adversely. Rather, it was advanced that anomalies are caused by the large particles giving an impulse to slow-sedimenting small particles.

### PARTICLE CLASSIFICATION

#### Elutriation

Elutriation is really the reverse of sedimentation. It consists of removing all the particles finer than a given size from a bed of particles by passing a stream of fluid, for example, air, through or over the powder bed. The particles removed are usually collected by filtration, and it is assumed that the fluid velocity is equal to the terminal velocity for the particles of the given size as calculated from Stokes' equation.

If the separation of particles is carried out in several steps, using successively greater fluid velocities, the sample is separated into a number of fractions according to particle size. The particle size distribution is obtained simply by weighing the fractions. A commercial instrument (100) based on Roller's work (101, 102) is claimed to give percentage weights that are reproducible to ±0.5%. Dallavalle (103) described a simple elutriator which is particularly useful for coarse size separation.

A common and inherent error in all elutriation techniques is that the fluid velocity is not constant across the ducts, so that the assumption of particle velocity equal to fluid velocity is usually invalid. In addition, the fractions obtained from elutriation do not have a sharp size distribution, so that average, estimated sizes have to be assigned. Moreover, it is fairly difficult to control the fluid speeds and still have the motion of particles laminar rather than turbulent.

#### Classification

Several commercial instruments (104, 105) that are based on particle classification through separation are available. Although, as discussed, these instruments give indeterminate particle size distributions because of the wide size ranges obtained, they are useful in studying the effect of particle size on properties of matter. Thus, if the stability of baking powder is found to depend on the particle size distribution, separation of one sample into several size fractions and then testing the stability would confirm or disprove the hypothesis. Size fractions obtained with the straightforward use of micromesh sieves (discussed in Chapter 7), however, might have as sharp a distribution as those obtained from classification methods.

Another version of elutriation is to use liquids (106, 107). Here the liquid is made to flow upward at a rate which is intermediate between the terminal velocities of the two fractions. Hence, the faster fraction will sediment downward, whereas the slower (finer-sized) fraction will be carried upward and can be collected from the overflow.

Other small- and large-scale classifiers have been annually reviewed by L. T. Work (108) since 1947.

**REFERENCES**

1. A. D. Hall, *J. Chem. Soc. Trans.*, **85**, 950 (1904).
2. T. Svedberg and K. Estrup, *Kollid-Z.*, **9**, 259 (1911).
3. G. G. Stokes, *Cambr. Phil. Soc. Trans.*, **8**, 287 (1849).
4. L. Page, *Introduction to Theoretical Physics*, D. Van Nostrand Co., New York, 1935, pp. 268–73.
5. J. C. M. Li and P. Chang, *J. Chem. Phys.*, **23**, 518 (1955).
6. J. Alexander, *Colloid Chemistry*, Vol. I, Chemical Catalog Co., New York, 1926, p. 404.
7. H. E. Rose, *The Measurement of Particle Size in Very Fine Powders*, Chemical Publishing Co., New York, 1954.
8. S. Chandrasekhar, *Rev. Modern Phys.*, **15**, 57 (1943).
9. G. J. Kynch, *Brit. J. Appl. Phys.*, *Supple. No. 3*, p. S5 (1954).
10. H. H. Steinour, *Ind. Eng. Chem.*, **36**, 901 (1944); **36**, 618 (1944).
11. G. J. Kynch, *Trans. Faraday Soc.*, **48**, 166 (1952).
12. G. Barr, *A Monograph on Viscometry*, Oxford University Press, London, 1931, Chapter VIII.
13. For details, see Chapter 2.
14. R. R. Irani and D. P. Ames, *Mater. Res. Stad.*, **1**, 637 (1961).
15. K. J. Mysels, *Introduction to Colloid Chemistry*, Interscience Publishers, New York, 1959, p. 44.
16. R. R. Irani, C. F. Callis, and T. Liu, *Ind. Eng. Chem.*, **51**, 1285 (1959).
17. A. I. Michaels *ASTM Spec. Tech. Publ. No. 234*, p. 207 (1958).
18. A. I. Michaels, T. L. Weaver, and R. C. Nelson, *ASTM Bull. No. 247*, p. 140 (1960).
19. E. H. Amstein and B. A. Scott, *J. Appl. Chem. (London)*, **1**, 510 (1951).
20. C. Rossi and R. Baldacci, *ibid.*, **1**, 446 (1951).
21. J. W. Lyons in J. R. Van Wazer, ed., *Phosphorus and Its Compounds*, Vol. II, Interscience Publishers, New York, 1961.
22. G. W. Phelps and S. G. Maguire, *J. Am. Cer. Soc.*, **40**, 399 (1957).
23. H. L. Vandersall and R. R. Irani, Unpublished results, Inorganic Chemicals Division, Monsanto Chemical Co., St. Louis 66, Mo.

24. F. Daniels, J. H. Mathews, J. W. Williams, and Staff, *Experimental Physical Chemistry*, fourth edition, McGraw-Hill Book Co., New York, 1949.

25. For example, (a)*Handbook of Chemistry and Physics*; (b) *International Critical Tables*.

26. A. H. M. Andreasen, *Ber. Deut. Keram. Ges.*, **11**, 249, 675 (1930).

27. A. H. M. Andreasen and S. Berg, *Angew. Chem.*, **48**, 283 (1935).

28. A. H. M. Andreasen, *Chim. Ind. (Paris)*, **70**, 863 (1953).

29. W. O. Hinkley, *Ind. Eng. Chem. (Anal. Ed.)*, **14**, 10 (1942).

30. S. Berg, *Ber. Deut. Keram. Ges.*, **33**, 229 (1956).

31. ———, *Ingn. Videns K. Skr.*, No. 2 (1940).

32. ———, *ASTM Spec. Tech. Publ. No. 234*, p. 143 (1958).

33. B. A. Jarrett and H. Heywood, *Brit. J. Appl. Phys., Suppl. No. 3*, 21S (1954).

34. H. A. Lorentz, *Abhandlungen über Theoretisch Physik*, Teubner, Leipzig, 1906, Vol. 1, p. 23.

35. G. J. Bouyoucos, *Soil Sci.*, **26**, 233 (1928).

36. A. Klein, *ASTM Spec. Tech. Publ. No. 51*, p. 52 (1941).

37. R. H. Lester, *Am. Ceram. Soc. Bull.*, **37**, 129 (1958).

38. D. G. Sammarone and H. S. Saunders, *ibid.*, **36**, 340 (1957).

39. C. V. Weaver, *J. Instr. Soc. Am.*, **1**, 24 (1954).

40. For example see E. E. Bryant and G. H. Johnson, *Am. Ceram. Soc. Bull.*, **38**, 649 (1959); S. G. Maguire and G. W. Phelps, *J. Am. Ceram. Soc.*, **40**, 403 (1957).

41. Technical Association of the Pulp and Paper Industry, TAPPI Designation T649 sm-54, Nov. 1954.

42. ASTM, ASTM Designation D422-54T, 1955. *Book of ASTM* Standards, Part 3, pp. 1756–66.

43. W. J. Kelly, *Ind. Eng. Chem.*, **16**, 928 (1924).

44. B. M. Abraham, H. E. Flotow, and R. D. Carlson, *Anal. Chem.*, **29**, 1058 (1957).

45. L. C. Bate and G. W. Leddicote, TID-7568 (Part 3), Office of Technical Services, U. S. Department of Commerce, Washington 25, D. C.

46. E. G. Richardson, *Trans. Inst. Min. Engrs. (London)*, **88**, 265 (1934); *J. Sci. Instr.*, **13**, 229 (1936).

47. H. E. Rose and H. B. Lloyd, *J. Soc. Chem. Ind. (London)*, **65**, 52, 65 (1946): manufactured by Evans Electroselenium, Ltd., Colchester Road, Essex, England.

48. N. A. Talvite and H. J. Paulus, *Rev. Sci. Instr.*, **27**, 763 (1959).

49. J. F. Brown and J. K. Skrebowski, *Brit. J. Appl. Phys.*, **53**, 27 (1954).

50. C. E. Marshall, *Proc. Roy. Soc. (London), Ser. A*, **126**, 427 (1930).

51. F. S. Eadie and R. E. Payne, *Iron Age*, **174**, 99 (1954); *Brit. Chem. Eng.*, **1**, 306 (1956). The instrument is merchandized by The Sharples Corp., 2300 Westmorland St., Philadelphia 40, Pa.

52. J. M. Dallavalle, *Micromeritics*, second edition, Pitman Publishing Corp., New York, 1948, Chapter 9.

53. D. P. Ames and T. P. Kichline, private communication from Monsanto Chemical Co., St. Louis 66, Mo.

54. D. Werner, *Trans. Faraday Soc.*, **21**, 381 (1925).

55. Bulletin on particle size apparatus, Palo-Myers, Inc., New York.

56. P. M. Travis, *ASTM, Bull No. 102*, 29 (1940).

57. K. T. Whitby, *Heating, Piping and Air Conditioning*, **61**, 449 (1955).

58. S. Oden, *Proc. Roy. Soc. Edinburgh*, **36**, 219 (1916).
59. J. Coutts and E. M. Crowthers, *Trans. Faraday Soc.*, **21**, 374 (1925).
60. E. W. Kanning, *J. Phys. Chem.*, **36**, 2370 (1932).
61. A. M. Gaudin, R. Schumann, and A. W. Schlechter, *J. Phys. Chem.*, **46**, 903 (1942).
62. W. Bostock, *J. Sci. Instr.*, **29**, 209 (1952).
63. P. Edwald, *Ind. Eng. Chem. (Anal. Ed.)*, **14**, 66 (1942).
64. D. P. Ames and R. A. Herrmann, unpublished results, Monsanto Chemical Co., St. Louis 66, Mo.
65. A. H. Nissan, *Discussions Faraday Soc.*, **11**, 15 (1951).
66. J. K. Donoghue, *Brit. J. Appl. Phys.*, **7**, 333 (1956).
67. S. Oden, *Soil Sci.*, **19**, 1 (1925).
68. T. Svedberg and H. Rinde, *J. Am. Chem. Soc.*, **45**, 943 (1923).
69. D. L. Bishop, *Bur. Standards J. Research*, **12**, 173 (1934).
70. I. W. Lohmann, *Rev. Sci. Instr.*, **21**, 999 (1950).
71. J. G. Rabatin and R. H. Gale, *Anal. Chem.*, **28**, 1314 (1956).
72. D. Bachmann and H. Gerstenberg, *Chem. Ing. Tech.*, **29**, 589 (1957).
73. Manufactured by Sartorius-Werke A. G., Gottingen, Germany. U. S. Agents: C. A. Brinkmann & Co., Inc., 115 Cutter Mill Road, Great Neck, Long Island, N. Y.
74. Manufactured by A. Gallenkamp Co., London, England. U. S. Agents: A. S. La Pine & Co., 6001 S. Knox Ave., Chicago, Ill.
75. D. P. Ames, R. R. Irani, and C. F. Callis, *J. Phys. Chem.*, **63**, 531 (1959).
76. E. H. Taylor and D. B. Harmon, *Ind. Eng. Chem.*, **46**, 1455 (1954).
77. C. P. Ross, *Anal. Chem.*, **31**, 337 (1959).
78. H. J. Kamack, *ibid.*, **23**, 844 (1951).
79. A. K. Gupta, *J. Appl. Chem. (London)*, **9**, 487 (1959).
80. K. T. Whitby, *J. Air Pollution Control Assoc.*, **5**, 120, 132 (1955).
81. ———, *Heating, Piping and Air Conditioning*, **61**, 449 (1955).
82. K. T. Whitby, A. B. Algren, and J. C. Annis, *ASTM Spec. Tech. Publ. No. 234*, p. 117 (1958).
83. Mine Safety Appliance Co., 201 N. Braddock Ave., Pittsburgh 8, Pa.
84. R. R. Irani and W. S. Fong, *Cereal Chem.*, **38**, 67 (1961).
85. O. Menis, H. P. House, and C. M. Boyd, O.R.N.L.-2345, Chemistry-General, Office of Technical Services, U. S. Department of Commerce, Washington 25, D. C.
86. C. M. Boyd, H. P. House, and O. Menis, TID-7568 (Part 3), Office of Technical Services, U. S. Department of Commerce, Washington 25, D. C., p. 56.
87. A. Romwalter and M. Vendl, *Kolloid-Z.*, **72**, 1 (1935).
88. C. Brown, *J. Phys. Chem.*, **48**, 246 (1944).
89. W. F. Sullivan and A. E. Jacobsen, *ASTM Spec. Tech. Publ. No. 234*, p. 98 (1958).
90. A. E. Jacobsen and W. F. Sullivan, *Ind. Eng. Chem.*, **18**, 360 (1946).
91. H. E. Robison and S. W. Martin, *J. Phys. Chem.*, **52**, 854 (1948).
92. ———, *ibid.*, **53**, 860 (1949).
93. J. K. Donoghue and W. Bostock, *Trans. Inst. Chem. Engrs. (London)*, **33**, 72 (1955).
94. T. Svedberg, *Ind. Eng. Chem. (Anal. Ed.)*, **10**, 113 (1938).
95. T. Svedberg and K. O. Pederson, *The Ultracentrifuge*, Oxford University

Press, London, 1940).

96. J. Alexander, *Colloid Chemistry,* Chemical Catalog Co., New York, 1926, Vol. I, chapter by T. Svedberg.

97. E. Saunders, *Anal. Chem.,* **20,** 379 (1948).

98. H. K. Schachman, *J. Phys. and Colloid Chem.,* **52,** 1034 (1948).

99. R. Johnson, *Trans. Brit. Ceram. Soc.,* **55,** 267 (1956).

100. Manufactured by American Instrument Co., Inc., Silver Spring, Md.

101. P. S. Roller, *Proc. ASTM,* **32,** Part II, 607 (1932).

102. ———, *J. Am. Ceram. Soc.,* **20,** 167 (1937).

103. J. M. Dallavalle, *Micromeritics,* Pitman Publishing Corp., New York, second edition, 1948.

104. B.A.H.C.O. Classifier distributed by the H. W. Dieteret Co., 9330 Roselawn Ave., Detroit 4, Mich.

105. Sharples Super Classifier, distributed by The Sharples Corp., 2300 Westmoreland St., Philadelphia 40, Pa.

106. G. G. Brown, *Unit Operations,* John Wiley and Sons, New York, 1950.

107. V. K. La Mer, R. H. Smellie, and P. K. Lee, *J. Coll. Sci.,* **12,** 566 (1957).

108. L. T. Work, *Ind. Eng. Chem.,* Annual Unit Operations Reviews, January issues (1947–1960).

chapter 6

___

# Microscopy

Microscopy is the most direct method for particle size distribution measurements. Theoretically, its range of applicability is unlimited; but practical limitations and availability of more expedient techniques make microscopy a less desirable tool in certain size ranges, as will be discussed later.

There are three distinct steps in making microscopic measurements: (1) slide preparation, (2) particle observation, and (3) actual counting and sizing of individual particles. The American Society for Testing Materials (ASTM) has recommended a procedure for analysis by light microscopy under ASTM designation E20-51T (1951). Parts of this procedure are used in some of the following sections.

Although research in microscopy is being actively conducted in numerous institutions, the field still retains "art" characteristics. This chapter is not intended to make a microscopist out of the reader. Rather, basic concepts required in making particle size distribution measurements from microscopy are presented. For those who wish to become closely acquainted with microscopy, several comprehensive books are available (1–5).

Microscopy can obviously be utilized to measure particle size distributions of a gas in liquid, liquid in liquid, or solid in liquid, etc. The techniques described here are mostly applicable for solids because they are the most abundant. For the other systems to be workable, it is necessary to have a large enough difference in refractive index between the particle and the medium to provide adequate contrast for particle observation.

## Specimen Preparation

Each application of microscopy generally necessitates the development of a specific technique to disperse and mount the particles. The general methods discussed in this chapter should be considered as some of the more common and applicable ones. An excellent collection of information on experimental techniques has been published by the Royal Microscopical Society (6).

One of the first steps in slide preparation is sampling. For the final results to be meaningful, the measured particles should be representative of a large quantity of material, of the order of tons in many cases. This necessitates taking several samples, mixing them thoroughly, and then sampling again. The reduced sample is then handled as described next.

## Dispersion

It it normally preferable to disperse particles in the same medium in which they will ultimately be used. Otherwise experimentation is required with combinations of various liquids and dispersing agents, as we have previously discussed in Chapter 5, to yield the required degree of dispersion. Tests for proper dispersion were also discussed in Chapter 5.

The most effective and general way for particle dispersion has been found to be spatulation, followed by vigorous stirring of the diluted slurry. A small amount of the powdered sample is placed in a flat glass plate and a few drops of the dispersion fluid are added; the high solid concentration gives a viscous medium. The powder is worked for a few minutes with a flexible spatula, using heavy pressure and a circular motion which is frequently reversed in direction. The viscous shear acts to separate the aggregates without shattering the individual particles.

The slurry is washed into a flask and more fluid is added until the particulate concentration reaches a desired value. The dilute suspension is then vigorously stirred with either ultrasonics or a high-speed homogenizer. The desirable particle concentration range is bracketed between an upper and a lower limit. The upper limit is dependent on the degree of attraction of the dispersed particles to one another; when mounted on a slide, the particles should be in one plane and properly separated to give individual particles rather than flocculates.

Particle-counting statistics impose the lower practical limit of particle concentration. It is well known that to obtain a representative particle-size distribution, we must count and size hundreds of particles. Obviously, if the particle concentration is so low that only a few particles are displayed in a single microscopic field, many fields have to be considered, making the technique less practical.

## Specimen Mounting

The mounting of particles on a slide depends on whether a light microscope or an electron microscope is used, and on whether or not a permanent mount is desirable. In a few cases, dispersion and mounting may be combined. Allen, for example, suggested (7) mounting powders directly in a clear cement, such as Duco cement. He suggested dispersing the material in cement, using sweeping strokes of a needle, and spreading a thin film of the dispersion on a glass slide to dry.

In light microscopy, the specimen is most commonly placed on a glass slide. When a nonpermanent mount is adequate, a drop of the dispersion is placed on the slide and a thin cover glass is utilized to hold the dispersion from flowing and evaporating. It has also been found successful to spray the dispersion onto the glass slide.

In some cases, where the flow properties of the powder are good, it has been found adequate to apply the dry powder directly on the slide either by puffing or by touching the slide with a brush that was previously dipped in the dry powder.

When a permanent mount of the particles onto a slide is desired, the mountant should be transparent, and the difference in refractive index between the vehicle and the particle should also be considered. If the difference is too great, contrast will be excessive, and edge detail may be lost. If the refractive index difference is too small, some particles may be missed.

The following materials have been used extensively as mounting media: collodion in amyl acetate, Canada balsam in xylol, rubber in xylol, and polystyrene in xylene. An example of mount preparation is as follows. A few drops of a 1% solution of collodion in amyl acetate are placed on the surface of water in an evaporating dish. The drops are hydrophilic, so they spread out over the water surface. The amyl acetate solvent evaporates readily, leaving a thin film of collodion floating on the water surface. This film can be easily transferred to the glass slide. Another method of preparing the mountant involves casting the film directly onto glass. It is, however, necessary to use a more dilute collodion solution, for example, less than ½%, because the mountant solution spreads over a smaller area on glass than on water.

After the mountant has been placed on the glass slide, the particle suspension can be sprayed on, or a droplet can be allowed to evaporate, leaving the particles. The particles become embedded into the mountant, forming a fairly permanent slide for future examination.

In electron microscopy the use of a mountant is imperative. This is true because a glass slide is not transparent to the electron beam. The mounting films mentioned are transparent to the electron beam if their thickness does not exceed a few hundred angstroms. With such a thickness, the films are too fragile to support themselves over a wide area and a small, circular wire grid (⅛ in. in diameter) is invariably used as a secondary support. The mesh is normally two hundred to the inch. A closer mesh would block out an excessive fraction of the total area, otherwise available for observation, whereas a looser mesh would not provide adequate support for the film. The grid may be either woven or electroplated, and it is commonly made out of copper or nickel.

The general method for transferring the mounting film from the surface of water onto the electron microscope grids is, first, to drop a number of clean grids onto the floating film. After about 1 minute, the grid with the film attached to it is picked up with a special circular loop.

The particles can be now applied to the film on the grid. This can be done either by placing a drop of the particle dispersion on the grid or by spraying the dispersion on. The latter technique has been found more desirable from the standpoint of giving well-dispersed particles. In either case, the fluid in the particle dispersion should obviously not dissolve the film.

One of the annoying problems encountered by electron microscopists occurs during the evaporation of droplets from suspensions on the specimen-supporting membranes. Aggregates are formed, particularly when samples are suspended in distilled water. Special plastic membranes are commercially available (Bitter Root Specialty Co., Hamilton, Mont.) to reduce this problem. These membranes are covered with a thin film of metal oxide, which does not reduce resolution of the micrographs. Since the metallic oxide layer is positively charged, negatively charged particles are readily deposited on the membrane in an evenly dispersed state.

For more details regarding specific applications and techniques in electron microscopy, see references 1–6.

## Particle Observation

Table 6-1 shows the particle size regions of applicability of several microscopic techniques. The lower limits are imposed by the attain-

### TABLE 6-1
### Regions of Applicability of Microscopic Techniques

| Method | Normal Size Range (microns) | Equipment Required |
|---|---|---|
| White light | 0.4–100 | Ordinary microscope, white light |
| Ultraviolet light | 0.1–100 | Microscope equipped with quartz optics, monochromatic light source |
| Ultramicroscopy | 0.01–0.2 | Microscope equipped for dark-field illumination, arc light source |
| Electron microscopy | 0.001–5 | Philips, RCA, Hitachi, Zeiss, Metropolitan-Vickers, or Siemens electron microscope |

able resolving power. Thus, a particle cannot be resolved if its size is close to the wavelength of the light source. In the ultramicroscope, the resolution is enhanced by using dark-field illumination (8). This kind of illumination is obtained when the light is so convergent that none of it enters the objective lens.

A trick that is commonly employed in light microscopy is to examine the very small particles in a fluid such as mineral oil in order to take advantage of the increase in refractive index difference between particles and fluid.

Diffraction of light prevents the resolution of points any closer than about 0.2 micron with a light microscope. Ultraviolet rays, with a wavelength range of about 100 to 4000 Å, provide a way of improving the resolution of a microscope. Nevertheless, the usual glass lenses employed in normal-light microscopy do not transmit ultraviolet rays, and other adequate lens materials must be utilized. The Bausch and Lomb Company manufactures a set of accessories to convert a light microscope into an ultraviolet microscope. A quartz mercury arc lamp is used with filters to permit the passage of ultraviolet light 0.037 micron in wavelength. The wavelength of electrons is of the order of few hundredths of an angstrom, and, indeed, careful electron microscopists have been able to resolve particles as small as 3–8 Å (9).

Resolution and magnification are two independent properties in microscopy. Thus, magnification is useless unless the image is perceptible by the human eye and the particle boundaries are well defined. The limiting resolution of the unaided human eye is about 0.1 mm.

The divergence among investigators concerning the maximum useful magnifications in various microscopes is due to slight differences in the instruments and techniques; microscopy still requires a good amount of operator technique. Lack of contrast is seldom a limiting factor in light microscopy because color staining can be utilized. In electron microscopy, there can be no staining to enhance the absorption of electrons (as takes place in light microscopy). Rather, an agent that scatters electrons readily should be utilized. This scattering is done by shadowing techniques.

The shadowing technique is probably the most useful single method of enhancing contrast in electron microscopy. Basically, it consists of increasing the density on sides of the particle so that the electron beam encounters a larger mass-density as it passes through these portions of the particle. Metals have been mostly utilized as shadowing materials. Silver, gold, chromium, uranium, and alloys are evaporated in a high vacuum system and deposited on the particle, as illustrated in Fig. 6-1. It is highly advantageous in shadow casting to use a point

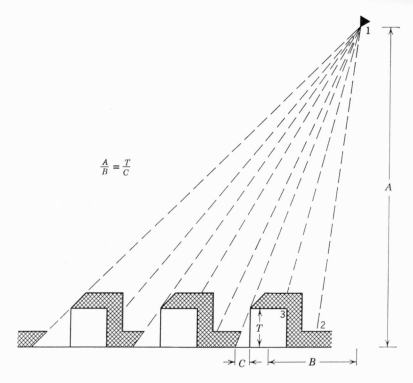

FIG. 6-1. Principle of shadow casting. (1) Source of shadowing material. (2) Supporting membrane and deposit. (3) Particle.

source of metal vapor in order to avoid uncertainties in deposit boundaries on the supporting membrane.

## Counting and Sizing

Before discussing details of particle counting and sizing, it is worth-
while to review special considerations regarding choice of particle
fields for that purpose, and the total number of particles that should
be counted.

Selecting the particulate fields that will be counted and sized is
another sampling step. It should preferably be done without prior
observation of the fields in order to avoid bias. The selection can be
either completely random or according to a previously chosen pattern,
such as certain positions on the mechanical stage. The total number
of fields to be counted depends on the number of particles per field,
and the minimum total number of particles that is representative of
the larger mother sample. Materials with uniform size distribution
require less particles to be counted than those with a broad size distribution. As a general rule, the number of particles measured should
be great enough so that the results do not change on measuring a
larger number. This is illustrated in Fig. 6-2 for the electronic counting and sizing of a monocalcium phosphate (10). It is shown that if
more than 400 particles are measured, then a representative particle

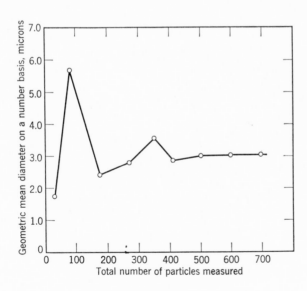

FIG. 6-2. Determination of minimum number of particles.

size distribution is obtained. This finding is very specific, and it is only applicable for the special combination of material and technique. The monocalcium phosphate sample that was studied was composed of particles having a relatively uniform shape, with the maximum-to-minimum-diameter ratio of any particle not exceeding three. Obviously, for materials containing odd-shaped particles, a larger number of particles must be measured.

One of the common mistakes in utilizing light microscopy for particle size measurement is to assume that the magnification of particles is given by the product of the nominal magnifications of the objective and eyepiece. Rather, a calibrated *stage micrometer*, available from microscope manufacturers, should be utilized to determine the magnification experimentally. A similar error can occur in electron microscopy.

The mounting of particles is another source of error. For example, when particles are mounted on a slide from a suspension, the larger particles may settle rapidly, whereas the smaller ones may be carried away, giving an uneven particle population. This difficulty makes spray mounting more desirable because all the particles reach the slide or grid simultaneously.

In microscopic particle size measurements only two dimensions can be measured. If the particles are peculiarly oriented, as is the case with platelets, the results will tend to be nonrepresentative. One way to circumvent the problem is to count the particles after they have been dispersed and embedded randomly in a transparent jelly. If a large number of particles is counted, all possible projections of a particle are considered. The average projected area of a particle is more representative than an oriented projection. In cases like this, which are rare, thousands of particles have to be counted and sized.

### Count Method for Average Size

The determination of average size by the count method is simple, but it does not give a size distribution. The total number of particles in a volume of fluid, containing a known weight of dispersed material, is measured with a microscope. The weight of an average particle is obtained by dividing the total weight by the number of particles. If the density of material is independent of particle size, the average volume of a particle is easily found, and from it a linear particle size can be assigned, by assuming either a cube or a sphere. In the former case, the cubic root of the average volume is calculated; in the latter case, the cubic root of $6/\pi$ times the average volume is computed.

In practice, if the material is a powder, the known mass is obtained by weighing it out, or, if it is already dispersed in a suspension, by chemical or physical analysis.

## Manual Visual Method

A direct particle size distribution can be obtained by visually measuring and classifying according to size images of particles seen either directly through the light microscope or from examining photomicrographs.

In light microscopy a graduated linear scale on the reticle of an eyepiece or a filar micrometer can be used to classify the particle size. The scales can be calibrated with a stage micrometer. If the particles are spherical, the largest diameter (major axis) is taken as the size. If the particles are not spherical, a problem arises as to which dimension should be measured. Martin (11) suggested that the line used in measuring the size be drawn in a direction so as to divide the image of the particle into two equal areas. He claimed that if a large number of particles is measured, representative sizes are collected.

Another classification method which is often utilized in manual sizing and counting is to compare the area of a particle with standard areas that are engraved (12) on the eyepiece reticle. Even for irregular particles, accurate evaluation and classification of size is approached by this method, because the whole projected area is considered rather than a specific dimension. If the particles are not oriented on the microscope slide, and a large enough number of them are measured, the measured particle size distribution is representative of the whole sample. Invariably, experience has shown that more reliable information (13) is obtained more rapidly with the area comparison method than with the linear-dimension comparison method. It should, however, be borne in mind that both methods rely heavily on the subjective judgment of a technician, and it is not rare for two technicians to assign sizes for the same particle that differ by more than 10%

## Microprojection Method

It has been reported by several investigators (14, 15) that measurement of projected particle images is advantageous. It magnifies the image and permits proper focusing of all the particles with varying depths. Loveland (16) recommends that the operator sit at a sloping desklike surface and view images projected from below. In this way the operator can comfortably follow the orientation of the particles and obtain their best measure.

The dimensions of the particle can be compared with linear scales, circles, hexagons, or even ellipses (16). Comparison should preferably be made with geometric figures having a shape similar to the particles.

### Photomicrograph Measurement

This method involves counting and sizing particles from a photomicrograph, either directly or by projecting the negative onto a screen (17). It has the inherent advantage of keeping a record of the measurement and getting desirable magnifications. It has the disadvantage over the visual method, however, that the focus was determined at the time the photograph was taken. When particles with different heights are present, the limitation of single focus becomes a drawback. If focus is adjusted with respect to the smaller particles, the larger ones may get out of focus and vice versa, so that it is sometimes more satisfactory to make two or more negatives of the same field differing in focus. Other details of photomicrography are found elsewhere (18).

### Automatic Counting and Sizing Equipment

Several automatic and semiautomatic scanning devices have appeared during the last few years for counting and sizing particles. Although they are rather expensive (automatic devices cost $10,000–$25,000), the manpower saved can justify the expense in some cases. In addition, since one of the limitations of microscopic measurements is the fact that they must count and size at least hundreds of particles, the use of electron devices that can do the job in few minutes has reactivated interest in microscopy. The subjectiveness of a technician in assigning a size to a particle is also eliminated. By being able to count in a reasonable period of time thousands of particles situated at random, all possible orientations of a particle are averaged out (see Chapter 2).

The particle size range of most automatic scanning devices depends on how the particles are presented. For example, with the Flying Spot Particle Resolver (to be discussed later), there is no limiting range. If the instrument is used in conjunction with a light microscope, the particle size range is 0.6–100 microns, whereas if electron photomicrographs are counted and sized (19), particles as small as 10Å can be measured. Very large particles can be photographically reduced in size to give a larger number of particles in each microscopic field. Knowing the magnification or reduction of size, the original particle size distribution can be back-calculated by taking a simple ratio. A brief description of some of the more useful commercial scanning units is presented next. A survey of techniques for automatic counting and sizing of particles has been made by Walton (20).

*Endter Particle-Size Analyzer*

Endter and Gebauer (21) constructed a semiautomatic instrument which requires that the imaged particles in the photomicrograph be recognizable by eye. Since the eye participates in the measuring process, the size of the particles to be measured in the photograph should not be less than 1 mm. Hence the magnification and enlargement of photomicrographs should bring the size of the smallest particles into this range.

A commercial instrument based on the following principle is available from Carl Zeiss Company of Germany: An iris diaphragm, illuminated from one side, is imaged by a lens in the plane of a Plexiglass plate. An enlargement of the micrograph is laid on this plate. By adjusting the iris diaphragm, the diameter of the sharply defined, circular, light spot appearing on the enlargement can be changed and its area made to coincide with that of the individual particles. When the measuring iris mark equalizes the area of a particle, a foot switch is depressed to register the count in the specific size channels; there are forty-eight size channels.

Although this instrument makes it very expedient to measure particle size distributions manually, it does not completely eliminate the subjective judgment of the operator in assigning a size for a particle.

*Flying Spot Particle Resolver*

The automatic commercial instrument, made by Cinema Television, Ltd., London, is based on the work of Roberts and Young and associates (22–24). It uses flying-spot scanning, a method of converting a two-dimensional density distribution into a varying voltage-time relation. An intense light spot slowly scanning a cathode ray tube is optically imaged down through a conventional microscope having a focusing substage. This imaged-down light spot scans a fixed microscopic field. The transmitted spot intensity alteration as received by a photomultiplier is amplified, counted, and monitored. Particle sizing is performed by pulse width selection; all pulses below the preset size are not recorded during the count. The results from the instrument correlate well with the ASTM E20-51T (1951) method (25).

Among the semiautomatic and automatic instruments, the Flying Spot Particle Resolver has been the most widely accepted. As previously mentioned, its particle size range is indeterminate and is dependent on the way the particles are presented to the counter.

*Casella Automatic Particle Counter and Sizer*

This instrument, made by Casella Electronics, Ltd., London, utilizes track scanning (26) for counting and sizing particles. The microscopic field is moved across the slit mechanically. The length of the slit intercepted by the particles determines the amplitude of the photomultiplier signal. This gives a measure of size for all particles lying wholly within the scan track. An edge correction is made by taking the difference between measurements obtained with two slits of different length. Therefore, complete size distribution curve can be obtained from a pair of scans by recording simultaneously the signals at various lengths using the appropriate discriminators.

## Particle Thickness

A microscope method of measuring thicknesses of fine particles has been described by Robbins (27). The principle of the method is to bring the particle into the space beneath a lens, resting on a plane surface, until the particle is in contact with both lens and plane. The thickness of the particle is then calculated from a knowledge of the radius of curvature of the lens and the distance of the particle from the point of contact of lens and plane, as illustrated in Fig. 6-3. The lens, of suitable curvature, can form part of an attachment to the substage condenser mount of a microscope. It was found from measurements on

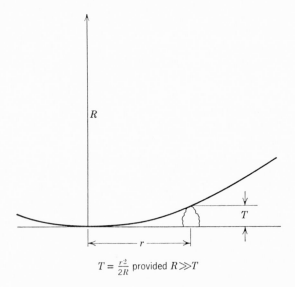

$$T = \frac{r^2}{2R} \text{ provided } R \gg T$$

FIG. 6-3. Principle of microscopic method for measuring thickness of particles. Here, $R$ is the radius of curvature, $r$ is the distance of the particle from the point of contact of lens and plane, and $T$ is the particle thickness.

spheres that particle thicknesses in the range of 3–100 microns can be measured with an accuracy of the order of 10%.

Another method for measuring particle thickness utilizes stereo-photogrammetric procedures (28). Best results, however, are obtained only with particles larger than 100 microns.

Shadow casting, previously mentioned as giving increased particle contrast, is also useful in evaluating the thickness of particles. Thus, referring to Fig. 6-1, the height of a particle, $T$, is simply

$$T = \frac{AC}{B}$$

where $A$ is the perpendicular height of the filament from the plane of the particle, $B$ is the distance from the point where the perpendicular from the filament intersects the plane of the particle to the particle, and $C$ is the shadow length.

These methods for determining particle thickness, although highly specialized, are very helpful in assigning shape factors to oddly shaped particles. Since microscopic techniques can only give a two-dimensional representation of particles, evaluation of the third dimension can be of value.

### Aerosol and Emulsion Examination

Even though the majority of the measurements involving microscopy have been done with solid particles, the technique is equally valid for emulsions and aerosols. The only restriction is to have a large enough difference in the refractive indices of particles and suspension to give a good contrast for counting and sizing. In both cases, photomicrographs are first taken and are then counted and sized.

Equipment for direct photomicrography of aerosol particles has been described by Cadle and Wiggens (29). It involves using a repeating flash tube system to produce incident, dark-field illumination of the aerosol. The duration of the flash can be adjusted between 1 and 10 microseconds. The reason for such fast photography is to "stop" the moving particles in the aerosol.

#### REFERENCES

1. E. M. Chamot and C. W. Mason, *Handbook of Chemical Microscopy*, Vol. I, third edition, 1958, Vol. 2, second edition, 1940, John Wiley and Sons, New York.
2. H. F. Schaeffer, *Microscopy for Chemists*, D. Van Nostrand Co., New York, 1953.
3. R. B. Fischer, *Applied Electron Microscopy*, Indiana University Press, Bloomington, Ind., 1953.

4. R. W. G. Wyckoff, *Electron Microscopy*, Interscience Publishers, New York, 1949.

5. C. E. Hall, *Introduction to Electron Microscopy*, McGraw-Hill Book Co., New York, 1953.

6. D. G. Drummond, *J. Roy. Micr. Soc., Ser. III,* **70**, 1 (1950).

7. R. P. Allen, *Ind. Eng. Chem. (Anal. Ed.)*, **14**, 92 (1942).

8. R. P. Loveland, *ASTM Spec. Publ. No. 143,* 1953.

9. J. Turkevich, *Science,* **47**, 97 (1959).

10. R. R. Irani, unpublished results, Research Department, Inorganic Chemicals Division, Monsanto Chemical Co., St. Louis 66, Mo.

11. G. Martin, *Trans. Ceram. Soc. (England)*, **23**, 61 (1923).

12. G. L. Fairs, *Chem. Ind. (London)*, **62**, 374 (1943).

13. R. J. Hamilton, J. F. Holdsworth, and W. H. Walton, *Brit. J. Appl. Phys., Suppl. No. 3*, p. 101 (1954).

14. E. J. Dunn, *Ind. Eng. Chem. (Anal. Ed.)*, **2**, 59 (1930).

15. R. P. Allen and G. S. Haslam, *Proc. ASTM,* **35**, Part I, 497 (1935).

16. R. P. Loveland, *ASTM Spec. Tech. Publ. No. 234,* p. 57 (1958).

17. H. Green, *J. Franklin Inst.,* **192**, 637 (1921).

18. C. P. Shillaber, *Photomicrography*, John Wiley and Sons, New York, 1944.

19. R. R. Irani and E. F. Kaelble, *Anal. Chem.,* **33**, 1168 (1961).

20. W. H. Walton, *Brit. J. Appl. Phys., Suppl. No. 3*, p 121 (1954).

21. F. Endter and H. Gebauer, *Optik,* **13**, 97 (1956).

22. F. Roberts and J. Z. Young, *Nature,* **167**, 1231 (1951).

23. F. Roberts, *ibid.,* **169**, 518 (1952).

24. F. Roberts and J. Z. Young, *Proc. Inst. Elec. Engrs.,* **99**, Part IIIA, 747 (1952)

25. D. P. Ames, R. R. Irani, and C. F. Callis, *J. Phys. Chem.,* **63**, 531 (1959).

26. D. G. W. Hawksley, *Brit. J. Appl. Phys., Suppl. No. 3*, p. 125 (1954).

27. W. H. M. Robbins, *Brit. J. Appl. Phys., Suppl. No. 3*, p. 189 (1954).

28. B. C. Aschenbrenner, *Photogrammatic Eng.,* **21**, 376 (1955).

29. R. D. Cadle and E. J. Wiggens, *Chem. Eng. News,* **31**, 3074 (1953).

*chapter 7*

# Sieving

Probably the simplest and most widely used method of determining particle size distributions is sieving. The method involves shaking the sample through a pair, or more commonly a stack, of several pans, each with a wire cloth bottom of smaller-size openings than the preceding one. The sample is separated into a series of fractions on the individual sieves.

Sieve analyses can be completed in a relatively short time, require little operator skill, and involve relatively inexpensive equipment. Until the recent introduction of micromesh sieves (1), the principal drawback to sieve analyses with woven sieves was that they could not be used for particles smaller than 50 microns because of the difficulty of weaving wire cloth having uniform openings of such small sizes. The recently available micromesh sieves extend the range of sieving tests to as low as 10 microns.

## Mechanics of Sieving

A thorough study of the physical laws that govern the sieving of fine particles has recently been completed by Whitby (2). In this work it was shown that the mechanism of sieving under non-steady-state conditions can be divided into two distinctly different regions with a transition region in between, as illustrated in Fig. 7-1.

Conventional woven sieves and the standard Tyler Ro-Tap were used in the study.

In region 1 there are many particles still on the sieve much smaller

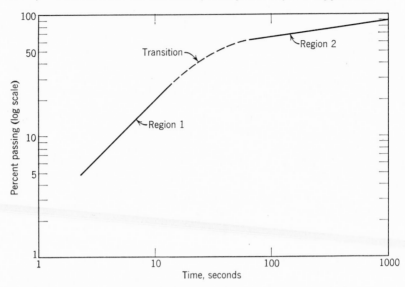

FIG. 7-1. Typical sieving curve. Reproduced from Whitby, *ASTM Spec. Tech. Publ. No. 234,* p. 4 (1958).

in size than the mesh opening. The cumulative weight fraction through the sieve at any time $t$ is given by the equation

$$\text{Fraction through} = C_1 \frac{\rho r S}{W_0} \left(\frac{S}{k_s M_g}\right)^{1/\ln \sigma_g} t^b \tag{1}$$

where $\rho$ is the density of the material, $S$ the mesh opening size, $M_g$ the geometric mean diameter on a weight basis of the original material on the sieve, $\sigma_g$ the geometric standard deviation of the material initially placed on the sieve (determined at the mesh size on the size distribution curve), $k_s$ a constant which is usually very nearly equal to one, $C_1$ a constant depending on the material sieved, $t$ the time of sieving, $b$ a constant usually slightly less than one, $r$ the fraction open area, and $W_0$ the initial sieve load per unit sieve area.

This relation has been shown to hold for wheat products, crushed quartz, St. Peter sand, glass beads, and other similar materials. The value of $C_1$ is dependent on the sieve motion and the specific material being sieved. The ranges of values of $C_1$ for Tyler Ro-Tap sieving is from about 0.5 for wheat flour up to about 5 for glass beads.

As the particles much smaller than the mesh size are removed, the sieving mechanism goes through a transition period and enters a second region. Here, all the particles much less than the mesh size have been eliminated from the residue and the particles remaining that can pass through the sieve are very near the mesh size. The cumulative percent through the sieve-versus-time curve has been found to follow the log-normal law, that is, plots are linear on log probability paper. The rate at which material passes through the sieve is expressed by the relation 2:

$$\frac{dC(W)}{dt} = \frac{100P_2}{t \log \sigma_g} \phi(Z) \tag{2}$$

where $dC(W)/dt$ is the percent by weight passing the sieve per unit time, and $P_2$ is a probability dependent on the material being sieved, the sieve motion and the type of sieve (that is, nylon, silk, wire, etc.):

$$P_2 = \frac{dN}{Nd(\log t)} = \log \frac{\sigma_g}{\sigma_{gt}} \tag{3}$$

$N$ is the number of particles that can pass through the sieve, $\sigma_{gt}$ is the reciprocal of the slope of the straight line on the log probability plot of the percent-through-versus-time curve at the size of the sieve mesh opening, $\phi(Z)$ is the normal probability function, $t$ is the time, and $\sigma_g$ is the same as defined for the relation of region 1.

Whitby (2) studied the laws described by equations 1 and 2 by varying sieve loads, sieve motion, material, relative humidity, and type of sieve and concluded that these equations represent the best fit over the broadest range of conditions of any sieving laws proposed to date. Most of such studies reported in the literature had been concerned with empirically fitting some sort of law to the results for a relatively narrow range of conditions. Variables investigated include sieve motion (3), loading (4), percent open area (5), calibration (6, 7, 8), static (9), humidity (7), and accuracy for a particular application (10, 11, 12, 13, 14).

### Types of Sieves

The common sieves used for particle size determinations are made with woven-wire cloth and have square openings. The sizes of screen openings have been standardized, and two standard series are used in the United States. These are the Tyler Standard Scale and the United States Sieve Series. The designations and dimensions of the two series are compared in Table 7-1.

The Tyler scale is based on the size of openings in wire cloth having 200 openings per linear inch (200 mesh). The diameter of the wire used for the 200-mesh screens is 0.0021 in. (0.053 mm), and the opening is 0.0029 in. (0.074 mm). The ratio between sizes of the scale is based

### TABLE 7-1
#### The Tyler Standard and United States Sieve Series

| | United States | | | | Tyler | | |
|---|---|---|---|---|---|---|---|
| | | Permissible Variation % | | | | | |
| Mesh No. | Openings (mm) | Av. Open. (±) | Max. Open.* (+) | Wire Diameter (mm) | Mesh No. | Openings (mm) | Wire Diameter (mm) |
| $3\frac{1}{2}$ | 5.66 | 3 | 10 | 1.28–1.90 | $3\frac{1}{2}$ | 5.613 | 1.65 |
| 4 | 4.76 | 3 | 10 | 1.14–1.68 | 4 | 4.699 | 1.65 |
| 5 | 4.00 | 3 | 10 | 1.00–1.47 | 5 | 3.962 | 1.12 |
| 6 | 3.36 | 3 | 10 | 0.87–1.32 | 6 | 3.327 | 0.914 |
| 7 | 2.83 | 3 | 10 | 0.80–1.20 | 7 | 2.794 | 0.833 |
| 8 | 2.38 | 3 | 10 | 0.74–1.10 | 8 | 2.362 | 0.813 |
| 10 | 2.00 | 3 | 10 | 0.68–1.00 | 9 | 1.981 | 0.838 |
| 12 | 1.68 | 3 | 10 | 0.62–0.90 | 10 | 1.651 | 0.889 |
| 14 | 1.41 | 3 | 10 | 0.56–0.80 | 12 | 1.397 | 0.711 |
| 16 | 1.19 | 3 | 10 | 0.50–0.70 | 14 | 1.168 | 0.635 |
| 18 | 1.00 | 5 | 15 | 0.43–0.62 | 16 | 0.991 | 0.597 |
| 20 | 0.840 | 5 | 15 | 0.38–0.55 | 20 | 0.833 | 0.437 |
| 25 | 0.710 | 5 | 15 | 0.33–0.48 | 24 | 0.701 | 0.358 |
| 30 | 0.590 | 5 | 15 | 0.29–0.42 | 28 | 0.589 | 0.318 |
| 35 | 0.500 | 5 | 15 | 0.26–0.37 | 32 | 0.495 | 0.300 |
| 40 | 0.420 | 5 | 25 | 0.23–0.33 | 35 | 0.417 | 0.310 |
| 45 | 0.350 | 5 | 25 | 0.20–0.29 | 42 | 0.351 | 0.254 |
| 50 | 0.297 | 5 | 25 | 0.170–0.253 | 48 | 0.295 | 0.234 |
| 60 | 0.250 | 5 | 25 | 0.149–0.220 | 60 | 0.246 | 0.179 |
| 70 | 0.210 | 5 | 25 | 0.130–0.187 | 65 | 0.208 | 0.183 |
| 80 | 0.177 | 6 | 40 | 0.114–0.154 | 80 | 0.175 | 0.142 |
| 100 | 0.149 | 6 | 40 | 0.096–0.125 | 100 | 0.147 | 0.107 |
| 120 | 0.125 | 6 | 40 | 0.79–0.103 | 115 | 0.124 | 0.097 |
| 140 | 0.105 | 6 | 40 | 0.063–0.087 | 150 | 0.104 | 0.066 |
| 170 | 0.088 | 6 | 40 | 0.054–0.073 | 170 | 0.088 | 0.061 |
| 200 | 0.074 | 7 | 60 | 0.045–0.061 | 200 | 0.074 | 0.053 |
| 230 | 0.062 | 7 | 90 | 0.039–0.052 | 250 | 0.061 | 0.041 |
| 270 | 0.053 | 7 | 90 | 0.035–0.046 | 270 | 0.053 | 0.041 |
| 325 | 0.044 | 7 | 90 | 0.031–0.040 | 325 | 0.043 | 0.036 |
| 400 | 0.037 | 7 | 90 | 0.023–0.035 | 400 | 0.038 | 0.025 |

* From No. 18 to No. 400, not more than 5% of the openings exceed the nominal opening by more than one-half of the permissible variations in maximum opening.

on a root of 2 and the ratio between the adjacent mesh sizes given in Table 7-1 is the fourth root of 2.

The United States Sieve Series proposed by the National Bureau of Standards uses the same ratio as the Tyler Standard Scale but is based on an opening of 1 mm (18 mesh). As can be seen from Table 7-1, the differences between the two series are small, and for most purposes the two sets of screens can be used interchangeably, particularly for the high mesh sizes.

A standard series adapted by the British Standards Institution and known as the British Standard Sieve Series has been used by the British since 1932. The ratio between sizes is the same as for the United States and Tyler series; however, there are slight differences between openings because United States and British standard wires are not quite the same. A German standard sieve series, known as DIN No. 1171, is designated by number and also by the number of meshes per square centimeter. The French use a similar series known as AFNOR.

Standards for sieve cloth and frames have been set up by the ASTM (15). These specifications require that the wire cloth be woven and not twilled (except the cloth for the 400, 325, 270, 250, and 230 mesh) from brass, bronze, or other suitable wire, and not coated or plated. Frames for all sieves of the fine series, No. 3½ or smaller, are circular and 8 in. in diameter, except that frames 3 in. in diameter may be used for sieves No. 100 and finer. The height of the sieve from the top of the frame to the cloth is either 2 in. or 1 in. The permissible variations in size of the openings are included in Table 7-1 and will be discussed later when we compare these woven sieves with the micromesh sieves (1). These ASTM specifications are tentative because some objection concerning wire diameters and tolerances was raised when they were offered through the American Standards Association to the International Standards Organization (ISO) for development of an international standard (16). The International Standards Organization is also considering a root-of-10 series.

Micromesh sieves made by electroforming nickel in meshes of precise square openings ranging from 10 to 120 microns are now commercially available (17). These sieves have been recommended for accurate particle size determinations on finer material than can be accurately measured with the woven-wire sieves (1, 18). Construction of the micromesh has been described (1) and involves basic photoengraving and electroplating techniques. The number of different sieves currently manufactured is limited by the availability of the expensive master rulings. Increased use of these sieves should lead to the making of additional master rulings and the manufacture of other sizes of sieves.

A microscopic comparison of the variations in uniformity of the mesh sizes of the two types of sieves as illustrated in Fig. 7-2 points

(a)

(b)

FIG. 7-2. Comparison of typical (a) woven-wire screens and (b) micromesh sieves.

up one of the basic advantages of the micromesh sieves. The manufacturer certifies the micromesh sieves to ±2 microns of the nominal value.

The permissible ranges of mesh openings for several woven-wire sieves as given by ASTM specification E-11 (15) (from Table 7-1) are compared with the measured sizes (1) of micromesh sieves in Fig. 7-3. Tentative specifications for precision micromesh sieves are given by ASTM E-161-60T, issued in June 1960. The closer tolerances of the micromesh sieves are evident from these comparisons.

### Calibration

The manufacturer of sieves determines the sizes of the openings and their variation with a microscope to see if the ASTM specifications

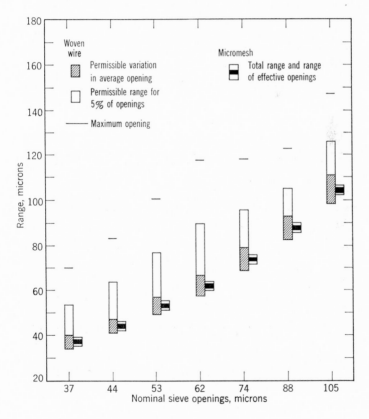

FIG. 7-3. Comparison of permissible ranges of openings in woven versus micromesh sieves.

(15, 19) are met. The National Bureau of Standards recommends measuring the diameter of five to ten wires, making four measurements for each wire. Then the number of wires per centimeter is determined and the average size of the opening calculated. Alternatively, sieves can be sent to the National Bureau of Standards for checking.

The user of sieves does not commonly calibrate them with a microscope, but he is advised to check new or shop-worn sieves with a standard sample to make sure that proper results are being recorded. Carefully sized fractions of glass beads are available from the National Bureau of Standards.

Recent studies with different materials have shown that accurate sieve analyses of fine powders can be assured only when the sieves are precalibrated with samples of the particular material whose size distribution has been determined by an independent method (20, 21). Sedimentation data on sieve cuts of different powders (20) show that for some powders the geometric mean diameter of the sieve cut as determined by sedimentation is approximately equal to the average diameter of the screen openings; whereas for other powders it is significantly different from the average of the two screen openings. This is illustrated in Fig. 7-4 with data for screen cuts of sodium isethionate and anhydrous monocalcium phosphate. The geometric mean diameter of the sodium isethionate from sedimentation is approximately equal

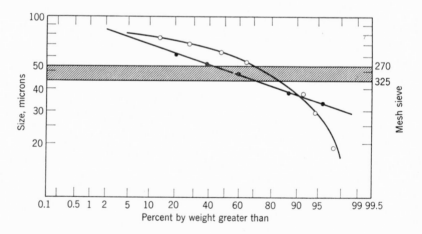

FIG. 7-4. Particle size distributions of sieve cuts. The white circles represent sedimentation data in 2-butanol for −270 mesh, +325 mesh anhydrous monocalcium phosphate; the black circles represent sedimentation data in 2-ethylhexanol for −270 mesh, +325 mesh sodium isethionate. Reproduced from *J. Phys. Chem.*, **63**, 533 (1959).

to the average diameter of the sieve openings, but for the calcium phosphate the geometric mean diameter from sedimentation is about 15 microns larger than the average of the sieve openings.

The typical sieving curve giving the percent passed through as a function of time and illustrated in Fig. 7-1 points up the fact that extremely long times are required for the amount passing through the sieve to reach a maximum value. In addition, the shape of the curve varies from one material to another. Therefore, in a practical analysis the selection of sieving conditions is very empirical. The results we have described for calcium phosphate and sodium isethionate are compatible with these general laws since the same arbitrary conditions were used for different materials with different sieving curves. The significant fractions of the cuts outside the nominal sieve opening are attributable to the wide range of the permissible limits on size openings.

Daeschner, Seibert, and Peters (1) recommend the calibration of the micromesh sieves by microscopic measurements of the size openings. A specific procedure for such a calibration is described in ASTM E-161-60T. The need for calibrating with samples of the material under investigation, however, has also been demonstrated for these sieves, even though the uniformity of the size of openings is far superior to that of the woven-wire sieves. Variation in assignment of the size of the openings with the material investigated is shown in Table 7-2 for three

TABLE 7-2

Calibration Data for Micromesh Sieves (18)

| | Assigned Size of Opening in Microns for Sieves[a] | | |
|---|---|---|---|
| Method of Calibration | A | B | C |
| With monocalcium phosphate[b] | 45 ± 3 | 23 ± 2 | 14 ± 1 |
| With glass beads[b] | 47 ± 2 | 33 ± 2 | 18 ± 1 |

[a] The sizes of openings determined microscopically are 44 ± 2, 28 ± 2, 20 ± 2 microns for *A*, *B*, and *C* respectively.

[b] Particle size distributions determined by sedimentation and electronic sizing and counting.

different micromesh sieves (18). These assignments were made by reading from size distribution data on the samples obtained by an independent technique the size that gave the same "percent greater than" as obtained experimentally with the sieve. The particle size distribution of the sieve cuts of the monocalcium phosphate as determined by sedi-

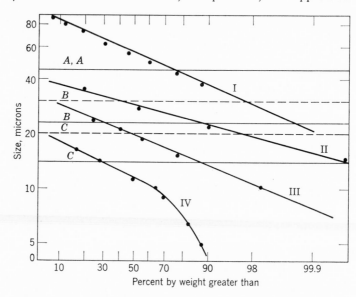

FIG. 7-5. Particle size distributions of micromesh sieve cuts of anhydrous monocalcium phosphate. I, +sieve $A$; II, —sieve $A$, +sieve $B$; III, —sieve $B$, +sieve $C$; IV, —sieve $C$. The solid lines show opening corresponding to calibration with sample. The dashed lines show opening from microscopic observation. Reproduced from *Anal. Chem.*, **31**, 2026 (1959).

mentation is shown in Fig. 7-5. Some coarser than the openings (by sedimentation) are passed through because of the shapes of irregular particles, and some particles finer than the openings are retained. This directly points up the necessity for calibration with a standard sample.

### Size Range of Applicability

It has been shown (20) for powders that are blocky in shape that woven-wire sieves can be used satisfactorily on material from "baseballs" down to powders with approximately 80% or more of the particles of sizes greater than 44 microns. This is shown in Fig. 7-6 for a sample of sodium isethionate where the particle size distributions determined by sieving and sedimentation are identical. In Fig. 7-7, however, where about 35% or more of the calcium phosphate particles are smaller than 44 microns, the sieve analysis becomes inaccurate and fails to distinguish between two powders with significantly different size distributions.

The micromesh sieves extend the range of the sieving method to

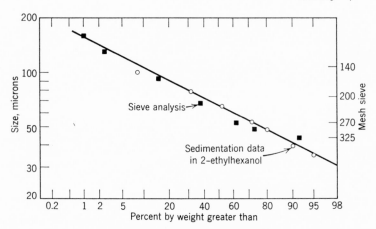

FIG. 7-6. The particle size distribution of sodium isethionate. Reproduced from *J. Phys. Chem.*, **63**, 533 (1959).

considerably smaller sizes. Satisfactory results have been obtained with powders having a geometric mean size on a weight basis of as low as 20 microns (18).

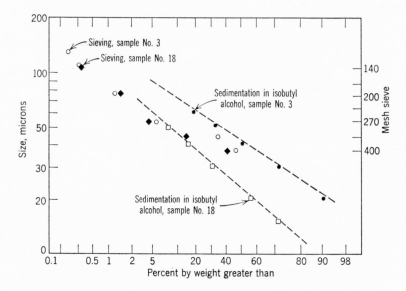

FIG. 7-7. Comparison of sieve analysis and sedimentation for anhydrous monocalcium phosphate powders with large fractions below 44 microns. Microscopic counting is represented by the dashed line. Reproduced from *J. Phys. Chem.*, **63**, 531 (1959).

## Special Techniques in the Measurement

The customary procedure in determining particle size distributions using sieves is to place a sample on the mesh of the top sieve of a nest of sieves, shake for a predetermined period of time, and weigh the portion of the sample retained on each sieve. Two systems are commonly employed for reporting the results: (1) the "$R$, $CR$, and $S$ system," where $R$ is percent retained on the largest sieve, $CR$ is the percentage cumulatively retained on the other sieves, and $S$ is the percentage passed through the smallest sieve; and (2) the "plus and minus system," where "plus" is the percentage retained on a sieve and "minus" is the percent passed through a sieve. Some experimental results (the same data) are expressed by both systems in Table 7-3. In the "plus and minus system" the percent total to 100, whereas in the "$R$, $CR$, and $S$ system" the percentage cumulatively retained on the smallest sieve plus the percentage screened through the same sieve add up to 100%.

### TABLE 7-3
#### Sieving Results Reported by Two Common Notations

| $R$, $CR$, and $S$ System (percent) | | Plus and Minus System (percent) | |
|---|---|---|---|
| $R + 20$ mesh | 3.0 | $+20$ mesh | 3.0 |
| $CR + 30$ | 25.0 | $-20, +30$ | 22.0 |
| $CR + 40$ | 55.0 | $-30, +40$ | 30.0 |
| $CR + 100$ | 96.0 | $-40, +100$ | 41.0 |
| $S - 100$ | 4.0 | $-100$ | 4.0 |

The importance of the conditions selected for analysis have been pinpointed in the extensive study by Whitby (2), reviewed earlier in this chapter. It should be reemphasized that the sieving is a highly empirical test because the sieving curve (Fig. 7-1) is not completely flat even in the second region of the process. More reproducible results would be expected, however, in the second region because of the less extreme change in the percent passing the sieve in a unit time. Therefore, the time of sieving should be selected so that the measurements fall in this second region. The ideal quantity of sample to be used is one that covers each sieve one particle deep (1); this means that the weight of sample should be reduced with the smaller sieves. On the other hand, a sufficiently large sample must be used to eliminate errors in sampling and weighing. Any particle agglomeration from generated static electricity or humidity changes must be eliminated, and the sieving motion and sample handling standardized.

A number of groups in the ASTM have adopted the use of sieves for particle size analyses on specific materials. The published standards are listed in reference 22. ASTM Committee C-21 on ceramic whitewares and related products, Task Group C, is investigating means of speeding up particle size analyses using micromesh sieves. This work includes the use of ultrasonic vibration as well as semiautomatic wet sieving.

The particle size committee of the American Association of Cereal Chemists is investigating (23) problems in sieve analysis of cereal products, and a review of principles and problems encountered is given in the reference article. The committee is considering a study of the possibilities of greatly reducing the time necessary for shaking a nest of sieves by the expedient of inserting a pan between each sieve so that the particles are in contact with all sieves at the beginning of a shaking period. Additional weighings would, of course, be required in such a procedure.

Mechanical shakers generally give more dependable results because of the reproducible action (24). Brushing has also been used sucessfully with the micromesh sieves (18). Whitby (2) found that in mechanical shaking with a standard Ro-Tap machine the most reproducible results and the faster through-put of material were obtained when a $\frac{1}{32}$-in. play was left between the cover plate and the sieves. This can be accomplished by placing a $\frac{1}{32}$-in. piece of cardboard under each hold-down lug with the bottom support slightly loosened. Then the sieve and cover plate are forced tightly upward against the cardboard under the lugs, the support is tightened, and the cardboard is removed.

Recently, equipment has been offered commercially (25) for vibrating a nest of sieves in a sieving operation. Very preliminary information indicates that on certain powders, at least, a faster through-put of material and less sieve blinding are achieved by the vibratory motion.

One very valuable technique that markedly increases the rate of sieving and minimizes sieve blinding with mechanical shaking is to add a small amount of a solid flow-conditioning agent. Irani and Fong (26), for example, found that the addition of 1% conditioner-grade tricalcium phosphate improved the flow properties of flour and, as a result, greatly facilitated the particle size measurement with the micromesh sieves.

**Wet Sieving**

Wet sieving is useful for materials originally suspended in a liquid (27), or for powders which form aggregates readily on dry shaking but which can be deagglomerated in a suitable liquid. Techniques for dispersing powders in liquids are described in Chapter 5. One disadvantage in wet sieving is the problem of determining the weight of dry material retained on the sieve; additional time is required to dry a sieve cut prior to weighing.

Several wet-sieving techniques have been found successful. The general procedure for woven sieves is to disperse the powder in a liquid, run the suspension through one or more sieves, and then pour additional liquid over the residue. Such a simple technique is not readily applicable to sieves smaller than 100 microns, for example, micromesh sieves, because of slower particle through-put. Three alternative procedures have been found successful with micromesh sieves. In one method, a dish is filled with sufficient fluid to cover the wire screen. One sieve is placed in the dish and with manual pumping action the fluid is washed up and back through the screen. The solution is changed as it becomes contaminated, and washing is continued until no more material is detected in the wash fluid.

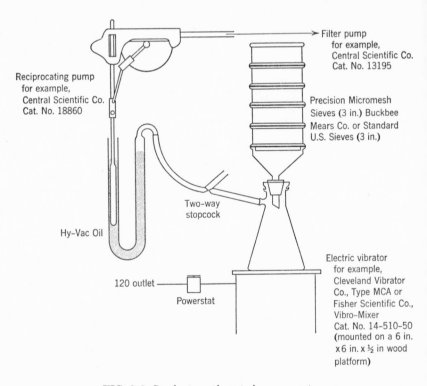

FIG. 7-8. Semiautomatic wet-sieve apparatus.

In another method, ultrasonic vibration energy is used. An ultrasonic tank is filled about quarter full with fluid. The sieve is immersed until it is about half full. The ultrasonic tank is activated, and a wash bottle is used to wash material clinging to the inside rim of the screen back onto the mesh. Sieving time has to be determined by trial and error for each material.

In another method, which is probably the most convenient, a set of sieves is mounted on an apparatus which vibrates an entire set of sieves as rapid alternate pressure and vacuum is applied to the meshes using a reciprocating water-aspirator pump. A schematic diagram with suggestions for parts is shown in Fig. 7-8.

**REFERENCES**

1. H. W. Daeschner, E. E. Seibert, and E. D. Peters, "Symposium on Particle Size Measurement," *ASTM Spec. Tech. Publ. No. 234* (1958).
2. K. T. Whitby, "The Mechanics of Fine Sieving," PhD. Thesis, U. of Minnesota, 1954; "Symposium on Particle Size Measurement," *ASTM Spec. Tech. Publ. No. 234* (1958).
3. A. W. Fahrenwald and S. W. Stockdale, Bur. of Mines, Reports of Investigations Serial No. 2933 (1929).
4. F. A. Shergold, *J. Soc. Chem. Ind.*, **65**, 245–9 (1946).
5. M. Weber, Jr., and R. F. Moran, "Precise Method for Sieving Analysis," *Ind. Eng. Chem. (Anal. Ed.)*, **10**, 180–4 (1938).
6. F. G. Carpenter and V. K. Deitz, *J. Res. Natl. Bur. Std.*, **47**, 139 (1951).
7. E. Moltini, *Ind. Mineraria (Rome)*, **7**, 771–84 (1956), *Appl. Mech. Rev.*, **11**, 345.
8. F. G. Carpenter and V. K. Deitz, *J. Res. Natl. Bur. Std.*, **45**, 328–345 (1950).
9. M. Allen, *Chem. Eng.*, **65**, 19, 176 (1958).
10. S. S. Fritts, *Ind. Eng. Chem.*, **9**, 180–1 (1937).
11. D. MacCalman, *Ind. Chem.*, **13**, 464 (1937); **14**, 64 (1938); **15**, 161 (1939).
12. L. Ackerman, *Chem. Eng. Mining Rev.*, **41**, 211–14 (1948).
13. H. Heywood, *Inst. Min. and Met. Bull.*, **477**, 18, March 1946. Also *Inst. Min. and Met.*, **55**, 373–90 (1946).
14. A. H. D. Marwick, *J. Soc. Chem. Ind. (London)*, 59, 88 (1940).
15. *1958 Book of ASTM Standards;* Tentative Specifications for Sieves for Testing Purposes, ASTM Designation E-11-58T, Part 3, 877–82. Also in Parts 4, 5, 7, 8, 9, 10. ASTM, Philadelphia, 1958.
16. L. T. Works, Introduction, "Symposium on Particle Size Measurement," *ASTM Spec. Tech. Publ. No. 234*, ASTM, Philadelphia, 1959.
17. Buckbee Mears Company, Toni Building, St. Paul 1, Minn.
18. R. R. Irani and C. F. Callis, *Anal. Chem.*, **31**, 2026 (1959).
19. See Table 7-1 for permissible limits of variations in sizes of openings.
20. D. P. Ames, R. R. Irani, and C. F. Callis, *J. Phys. Chem.*, **63**, 531 (1959).
21. J. R. Johnson and J. S. Newman, *Anal. Chem.*, **26**, 1843 (1954).
22. B214, *1958 Book of Standards*, Part 3; C92, C285, C325, C371, *1958 Book of Standards*, Part 5; C117, C136, C142, C184, C239, D313, D422, D451, D452, D456, D1140, E20, *1958 Book of Standards*, Part 4; C430, 1959, Supplement to *Book of ASTM Standards*, Part 4; D185, D197, D292, D310, D311, D410,

D431, D480, D715, D717, D718, D1214, *1958 Book of ASTM Standards,* Part 8; D392, D1507, D1508, D1511, D1514, *1958 Book of Standards,* Part 9; D502, *1958 Book of ASTM Standards,* Part 10.

23. "Sieve Analysis of Cereal Products," Report of the AACC Particle Size Committee, *Cereal Science Today,* **6**, 31 (1961).

24. C. Orr, Jr., and J. M. Dallavalle, *Fine Particle Measurement,* The Macmillan Co., New York, 1959, p. 38.

25. NoVo Division, Industrial Enterprises, Inc., 9705 Cottage Grove Avenue, Chicago 28, Ill.

26. R. R. Irani and W. S. Fong, *Cereal Chem.,* **38**, 67 (1961).

27. P. G. Meerman, *Verfkroneik,* **20**, 35–6 (1947).

# chapter 8

# Miscellaneous techniques

In the last three chapters, the major techniques for particle size distribution measurements, namely, microscopy, sedimentation, and sieving, were discussed. There are, however, several other useful techniques, which were not covered because of their limited and specific applicability. Table 8-1 is a concise summary of these techniques, including the size range applicable, usefulness, equipment required, elapsed time per determination, and approximate cost. Of these "miscellaneous" techniques, however, adsorption, permeametry, cascade impactor, light scattering, and change in electrolytic resistivity (the Coulter Counter) will be briefly and separately discussed because of their wider utilization. In addition, the methods for particle size measurement of aerosols are tabulated in Table 8-2 at the end of this chapter.

### AVERAGE SIZE FROM PERMEAMETRY

Methods based on permeametry for measuring the average particle size have received a lot of attention. This attention is due to the virtues of extreme simplicity of operation, and the rapidity of obtaining results, usually within a few minutes.

Generally, a permeability apparatus consists of a chamber for the material to be measured, and a device to make the fluid, gas or liquid, flow through the powder bed. The pressure drop and rate of flow across the powdered bed are measured and related to an average particle size, using the known powder bed dimension and degree of packing.

## TABLE 8-1

### Miscellaneous Techniques for Particle Size Determination

| Technique | Size Distribution[a] | Useful on | Normal Size Range (Microns) | Equipment Required | Approx. Elapsed Time per Determination[b] | Approx. Cost[c] | Ref. |
|---|---|---|---|---|---|---|---|
| Permeametry | No | Powders | 0.5–50 | (a) Fisher Sub-Sieve Sizer (b) Blaine Permeameter (c) Other special equipment | 15 Minutes | $300 | See discussion |
| Adsorption | No | Powders | 0.01–10 | (a) BET gas adsorption apparatus or Perkin-Shell Sorptometer (b) Common lab. equipment for adsorption from solution (c) Calorimetric apparatus for heat of immersion | 1–2 Hours | $2500 | See discussion |
| Light scattering | Difficult | Powders, emulsions, suspensions | 0.05–1.0 | Photometer; for example, Brice-Phoenix | Hours | $1500 | See discussion |
| Change in electrolytic resistivity | Yes | Powders, bubbles, emulsions, suspensions | 2–100 | Coulter Counter (marketed by Coulter Indl. Co., Elmhurst, Ill.) | 1 Hour | $5000 | See discussion |
| Cascade impactor | No | Air-borne particles, aerosols | 0.1–100 | (a) Casella-Sonkin (marketed in U.S. by Mine Safety Appliance Co.) (b) Home-built, more accurate and reliable than (a) above. | — | $1000 | See discussion |
| X-Ray low-angle scattering | No | Powders | 0.01–10 | X-Ray diffraction equipment plus special attachment | Hours | $15,000 | 1 |
| Sonic vibrations | Possible | Powders, liquid, contaminants | Limited | Sonic generator | Minutes | $1000–5000 | 2 |
| Bulk density and rate of packing | No | Powders | Limited | Common lab. equipment | Minutes | — | 3, 4, 5 |
| Magnetochemistry | No | Powders | 0.005–10 | Equipment for magnetic measurements | Hours | — | 6 |
| Precipitation of charged particles | No | Aerosols | 0.2–1.5 | Home-made precipitator, voltmeter, potentiometer | — | — | 7 |
| Reflectance | No | Colored emulsions, emulsion kinetics | 1–60 | Special cells, pulse generator, dual-beam cathode ray oscillograph | — | — | 9–11 |
| Light scatter decay | No | Aerosols, fine powders | 1–10 | Home-built | — | — | 12 |

[a] "No" means only an average size is obtainable.
[b] Estimated.
[c] These are rough estimates and do not represent quotations from manufacturers. Obviously, the cost of home-built devices is difficult to assess.

The flow of fluid may be either streamline or Knudsen. The former flow pattern has found more applicability.

Permeametry is a technique for measurement of surface areas. The pressure drop observed in permeametry is related to the surface area which the fluid contacts. For completely nonporous materials, the contact area can be unambiguously defined. For porous materials, the fluid passes through some but not all of the cracks. Therefore, the surface areas obtained from permeametry are intermediate between the external and internal surface areas; the full surface area is defined as the total sum of the external and internal surface areas.

### Streamline Flow

The equations governing the streamline flow of fluids through a powdered bed are complex and semiempirical. Actually there are several equations (13), but all of them show that fluid flow is proportional to the square of the particle size and to some power of the porosity. The equation that has been most popular (14, 15) is the Kozeny-Carman:

$$S^2 = \frac{gL}{2\eta V L_e \rho^2} \frac{\Delta P}{L} \frac{\Theta^3}{(1 - \Theta)^2}$$

where $S$ is the surface area per unit weight of solids, $g$ the acceleration due to gravity, $L$ the length of the packed powdered bed, $L_e$ the length of path of the fluid, $\eta$ the viscosity of the fluid, $V$ the velocity of fluid flow, $\rho$ the solid density, $\Delta P$ the pressure drop, and $\Theta$ the void fraction in the particular packing.

In normal measurements the ratio $L_e/L$ is unknown and has been reported to depend on both the specific material and the geometric shape of the particles (16). Values for the ratio $L_e/L$ ranging from 1.5 for cylinders arranged parallel to flow, for example, fibers, to 3.0 for cylinders arranged perpendicular to flow have been reported (17). For spheres the ratio has been found to be 2.25. Earlier, Carman (18) found that for a large number of powders with irregular particles the ratio $L_e/L$ is 2.5.

### Methods Based on Permeametry

The problems that arise in utilizing permeametry for the measurement of particle size are largely due to the necessity of having to utilize semiempirical equations with parameters that cannot be evaluated directly.

Gooden and Smith (19) constructed one of the first workable apparatus based on permeametry. The apparatus measured the flow rate of gas through a powder bed under a controlled pressure differential. A commercial instrument based on this principle, the Fisher Sub-Sieve Sizer, has been produced and sold with success. A graphic method is utilized to eliminate calculations and to give average particle size directly. Recent controversies about the method are due to the misinterpretation of the region of applicability and of the equations underlying the method. Thus, for porous and irregular particles, an average particle size is obtained which does not correlate with results from microscopy or BET surface area measurements.

The Kozney-Carman equation is based on streamline flow of fluid, so that presence of submicron particles upsets the assumption. Submicron particles negate the assumption of streamline flow because they agglomerate readily, and flow mechanism in beds of submicron particles is largely molecular (20). Therefore, air permeability apparatus should not be utilized on materials containing submicron particles. Actually, Hutto and Davis (20) showed that the Fisher Sub-Sieve Sizer should be used only for materials with surface areas lying in the narrow range of 0.05–2.25 sq m/gm.

Another popular apparatus is the Blaine permeameter (21), which is a simple form of air permeability apparatus. A commercial model is offered by the Precision Scientific Co., Chicago, for about $150. In this instrument, air is caused to flow through a powder bed by the pressure of oil displaced from equilibrium in two chambers which are connected to the permeability cell and to each other in a U-tube. The oil level in one arm is displaced by reducing the pressure. Then the time required for oil to fall from one level to another is measured. The rate of fall depends on the particle size of the material and the porosity of the packing: $S = k \sqrt{t}$ where $S$ is the surface area per unit weight, $t$ the time of fall of liquid between two levels in the U-tube, and $k$ is a constant which depends on the physical constants of the permeameter and the porosity of the powdered bed. In practice, values of $k$ are available for various porosities from calibration with powders whose specific areas on a weight basis are known.

The cement industry has found the Blaine permeameter to be useful, and an ASTM procedure, C204-55, based on air permeability has been adopted. The porosity of the powdered bed is evaluated by filling the voids with mercury and weighing. From the known density of mercury at various temperatures, the void fraction is calculated.

Ober and Frederick (22) have made a thorough study of the Blaine permeameter. They concluded that the equations in ASTM designation C204-55 are in some error because of inadequacies in assessing the effect of porosity on the results and not adequately describing the permeability of the powdered bed. They proposed to include another constant in the equations. Although the inclusion of a correction factor seems to give better agreement between the results from the Blaine permeameter and those from conventional BET nitrogen adsorption, its value must be evaluated experimentally for the special system being investigated.

A special permeameter for measuring particles in the range of 0.02–5 microns has been constructed (23, 24). The equations, however, are more complicated because of corrections for slip flow (molecular flow). The results agree fairly well with those from gas adsorption (25).

If gaseous flow is made to occur under very small pressures, the mean free path of the gas molecules becomes larger than pore dimensions and the flow is called Knudsen. From measurements of the time necessary for establishment of steady flow through a powdered porous mass, Barrer et al. (26, 27) obtained surface areas that included the blind pores:

$$S = \frac{8\Theta}{1 - \Theta} \frac{t}{L^2} \sqrt{\frac{2RT}{\pi M}}$$

where $S$ is the surface area, $\Theta$ the void fraction, $t$ the time necessary for establishment of gas steady-state flow, $L$ the length of powdered porous mass, $R$ the gas constant, $T$ the absolute temperature, and $M$ the molecular weight of the gas. Nevertheless, as with other permeability methods, modifications of the given equation have been published (28).

The rate of flow of liquids through a powdered bed has been also used for particle size measurements (29) with various degrees of success. For coarse particles in the range of 70 to 100 mesh, close agreement between liquid permeametry and microscopy was found, whereas for finer materials large deviations, of the order of 50%, were found from comparing the data with nitrogen adsorption (30).

In summary, the permeability technique has received a lot of attention and many improvements have been incorporated into the theory. No completely satisfactory theory has been developed as yet, however, that is as sound as Stokes' law, for example. Only an average size is obtained, and the nature of this average is not rigorously known. Nevertheless, the simplicity, low expense, and speed of the technique have made it attractive to many institutions with many routine measurements. Perhaps it is in the measurements on fibers in the textile industry that the permeability technique offers advantages unequaled by other known methods (16, 31–33). Commercial instruments for use with fibers are the Micronaire made by the Sheffield Corporation, Dayton, Ohio, and the Arealometer and Speedar made by the Special Instruments Laboratory, Inc., Knoxville, Tenn.

## AVERAGE PARTICLE SIZE FROM ADSORPTION METHODS

The basis for the measurement of an average particle size from adsorption methods is the fundamental relations between the size $M$, surface area per unit weight $S$, and volume per unit weight $V$ of a particle. In general, if the weight of the particle is $\omega$, then

$$S = \frac{\alpha M^2}{\omega} \tag{1}$$

$$\omega = \rho V = \rho \beta M^3 \tag{2}$$

where $\rho$ is the density of the material and $\alpha$ and $\beta$ are constants. From equations 1 and 2,

$$M = \frac{\alpha/\beta}{\rho S} \tag{3}$$

When a large number of particles are considered, average values for $M$ and $S$ are obtained. For spherical particles $\alpha$ and $\beta$ are $\pi$ and $\pi/6$ respectively, and the ratio $\alpha/\beta$ equals 6. Since a spherical particle has the smallest possible surface-to-volume ratio, any deviation from spherical shape will lead to an increase in the actual surface-to-volume ratio and yield an average particle size value that is smaller than the actual average particle size. The only exceptions to this general rule are perfect cubes. The effect of particle shape can be partially corrected for by knowledge of the actual shape of the particle under consideration. Unfortunately, powdered materials are usually composed of particles having a number of shapes. In these cases, an average value for the ratio $\alpha/\beta$ can be utilized to correct partially for the deviations.

Adsorption methods yield surface areas that include both the external surface of the particles and the internal surface due to pores, fissures, or cracks. Particles with significant internal-surface areas are usually called porous particles. Since there is no known way to easily separate the portion of the surface areas attributable to pores from the total surface area, adsorption methods can yield a physically meaningful average particle size only with nonporous materials. This is the most severe limitation of adsorption methods in particle size analysis. For porous materials it can lead to discrepancies of up to several orders of magnitude, with the particle size computed from adsorption methods always giving the smaller value. For example, over 90% of the total surface area of diatomaceous earth clay particles is due to their internal pores. The same is true for many flow-conditioning agents (34, 35).

Another effect that causes particle size values from adsorption techniques to be erroneously small is surface roughness. Since adsorption methods determine how much gas or vapor is required to form a unimolecular layer of atoms or molecules, surface irregularities of molecular or larger dimensions contribute to the measured surface area and give rise to a calculated particle size that is too small.

From the foregoing discussion, it is obvious that extreme care must be exercised when attaching physical significance to a particle size computed from surface area measurement. For nonporous materials, the errors introduced by nonspherical shape and surface roughness are not very serious (36). Nevertheless, it is well known that surface area measurements by gas adsorption are not too precise for values below 2 sq m/gm. A hypothetical material with a specific gravity of 2 and composed of spheroidal, monosized, 1-micron, nonporous particles has a specific surface area of 6 sq m/gm. Therefore, when using gas adsorption to determine an average particle size of nonporous materials, we should note that the practical upper size limit for precise results is about 2–3 microns.

As shown in Table 4-2, the average particle size obtained from adsorption methods for nonporous materials is related to the geometric mean sizes obtained from microscopy (number average) and sedimentation or sieving (weight average). For powders whose particle size distribution is log-normal, equation 3 can be written as

$$S = \frac{\alpha/\beta}{\rho M_n \exp\ (2.5\ \ln^2\ \sigma_n)} \tag{4}$$

or

$$S = \frac{(\alpha/\beta)\ \exp\ (0.5\ \ln^2\ \sigma_g)}{\rho M_g} \tag{5}$$

where $M_n$ and $M_g$ are the geometric mean sizes on a number and weight basis respectively, and $\sigma$ is the geometric standard deviation, as discussed in Chapter 4.

This discussion shows that if the density and the shape of the particles and the specific surface area of a material are known, a surface average particle size can be readily calculated. Methods for determining particle density were presented in Chapter 5.

A large amount of work has been done during the past thirty years on methods for determining specific surface areas of solids. We only cover the fundamentals, and we refer the interested reader to authoritative textbooks on the subject (37–42).

There are two general kinds of adsorption, namely, chemisorption

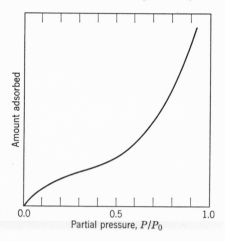

FIG. 8-1. Typical adsorption isotherm.

and physical adsorption. In chemisorption there is a significant interaction between the adsorbent and the adsorbate with the heat of sorption being large, normally larger than 15 kcal/mole. In physical adsorption, the forces holding the adsorbate to the adsorbent are weak and are primarily due to Van der Waals forces. Physical adsorption is used in specific surface area determination.

In making surface area measurements we determine the amount of gas or solute in a liquid adsorbed on a solid at a constant temperature as a function of gas pressure or concentration to obtain the so-called adsorption isotherm. A typical gas adsorption isotherm is shown in Fig. 8-1. From the adsorption isotherm we calculate the amount $X$ of adsorbate required just to cover the surface of a unit weight of adsorbent. The specific surface area per unit weight, $S$, is then

$$S = \frac{X}{\text{M. Wt.}} \times N \times A_0 \qquad (6)$$

where M. Wt. is the molecular weight of the adsorbate, $N$ is Avogadro's number, and $A_0$ is the area occupied by a single molecule of adsorbate. Unfortunately, the value of $A_0$ is not independent of the adsorbent. For the commonly used nitrogen gas, values for $A_0$ in the range of 10–16Å have been reported.

## Gas Adsorption

The volume or weight of adsorbed gas as a function of partial pressure has been used to determine the adsorption isotherm. In both cases a high vacuum is required.

Most volumetric apparatus are based on the design first used by Emmett (43). Blueprints of a slightly improved design are available from the Mellon Institute, Pittsburgh, Pa.

Gravimetric apparatus, first used by McBain et al. (44), are usually harder to construct than volumetric apparatus. They also suffer from the disadvantage of the requirement of measuring very small changes in weight.

Using a spring balance and an optical system in the gravimetric adsorption method, Milligan et al. (45) described an apparatus suitable for simultaneous adsorption measurements on fifteen samples. Klevens et al. (46) utilized a linear variable differential transformer (LVDT) to construct a recording gravimetric adsorption apparatus. The core of the LVDT was directly connected to the spring balance so that weight changes were directly converted to a voltage that was amplified and recorded.

A promising new approach to the measurement of surface area by gas adsorption was recently reported (47). It employs an apparatus similar to that employed in vapor phase chromatography. Nitrogen is adsorbed by the sample at liquid nitrogen temperature from a gas stream of nitrogen and helium and later eluted on warming the sample. The nitrogen adsorbed and later liberated (desorption) is measured by thermal conductivity. A commercial instrument based on this principle is now available from Perkin-Elmer under the trade name Sorptometer. Typical data are shown in Fig. 8-2, with the area under the curve being proportional to the amount of adsorbed nitrogen.

Although many theories on adsorption have been advanced during the past half century, Brunauer, Emmett, and Teller's equation (48), commonly referred to as the BET equation, is still the most useful in calculating monolayer adsorption. The equation is:

$$\frac{y}{V(1-y)} = \frac{1}{V_m C} + \frac{(C-1)y}{V_m C} \tag{7}$$

where $y$ is the relative pressure, that is, the ratio of the equilibrium pressure to the saturation pressure at a specific temperature, $V$ the amount of gas adsorbed, and $V_m$ the value of $V$ for monolayer coverage. The constant $C$ is related to the energies of adsorption and gas liquification:

$$C = \exp\left(\frac{F^\circ_1 - F^\circ_L}{RT}\right) \tag{8}$$

where $F^\circ_1$ is the standard Gibbs free energy of adsorption in the first layer and $F^\circ_L$ is the Gibbs free energy of condensation of the adsorbate (49).

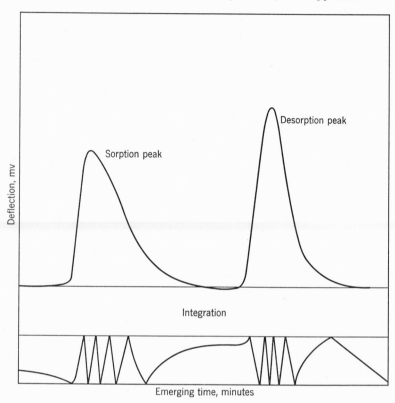

FIG. 8-2. Typical chart for nitrogen adsorption using Perkin-Elmer's Sorptometer for a partial pressure of 0.3.

A plot of $y/V(1-y)$ versus $y$ is normally linear for the range of partial pressure $(y)$ of 0.05 to 0.4 with a slope of $(C-1)/V_mC$ and an intercept of $1/V_mC$. It can be easily shown that $V_m$ is the reciprocal of the sum of the intercept and slope of such a line.

### Adsorption from Solution

Adsorption from solution has been represented by two different equations. The classical Freundlich adsorption isotherm (50) for molecules or ions on solid surfaces is:

$$X = kC^{1/n} \qquad (9)$$

where $X$ is the amount adsorbed per unit weight of adsorbent, $C$ is the concentration of adsorbate in the solution at equilibrium, $k$ is a constant, and $n$ varies between 1 and 10. Freundlich's equation implies that as the concentration of adsorbate increases, the amount adsorbed increases. In practice, this has not been found to be the case, probably because of the saturation of the adsorbent surface with adsorbate. Moreover, in surface area determination, it is the state of monomolecular surface saturation that must be determined. Therefore, equation 9 cannot be utilized for surface area determination.

Langmuir (51) used a kinetic approach of sorption-desorption equilibria to show that in dilute solutions

$$X = \frac{abC}{1 + bC} \tag{10}$$

where $b$ is related to the heat of adsorption, $Q$, by the equation:

$$b = b' \exp\left(\frac{Q}{RT}\right) \tag{11}$$

From equation 10 it is apparent that, as $C$ increases in value, $X$ approaches $a$. Therefore, $a$ is the value of $X$ for surface saturation. Qualitatively, then, $a$ is a measure of the surface area of the solid, and $b$ is a measure of the strength of adsorption.

The value of $X$ for a monolayer may be determined directly as the limiting value approached at high concentration or, indirectly, if the isotherm fits the Langmuir equation. It is convenient when testing the fit of the equation to the experimental data to put equation 10 in its linear form:

$$\frac{C}{X} = \frac{1}{ab} + \frac{C}{a} \tag{12}$$

Thus a plot of $C/X$ versus $C$ gives a straight line with a slope of $1/a$ and an intercept of $1/ab$.

If $X$ is in moles of adsorbate per gram of adsorbent, and the specific surface area $S$ is desired in square centimeters per gram, then:

$$S = aN\sigma^\circ \tag{13}$$

where $\sigma^\circ$ is the actual area of one adsorbate molecule in square centimeters, and $N$ is Avogadro's number. As with the gas adsorption method, it is necessary to make some assumption as to the value of $\sigma^\circ$. In low-temperature gas adsorption, essentially symmetric molecules such as $N_2$ and $O_2$ are involved, so that molecular areas can be estimated from liquid or solid densities. In the case of adsorption from solution it is usually necessary to assume some particular orientation in estimating $\sigma^\circ$ since more complex and consequently less symmetric molecules are involved.

It can be clearly concluded that it is feasible to make surface area estimations by means of adsorption from solution. In addition, such methods are more rapid and require less apparatus than does gas adsorption. The dangers of obtaining misleading results are appreciable, however. It is difficult to prove the absence of multilayer adsorption, and the adsorbed layer may contain solvent, so that the adsorbate at the monolayer fails to occupy the expected area per molecule. For example, it has been reported (52) that fatty acids and alcohols adsorbed from aqueous solution on Graphon® varied in area of actual molecular contact with the surface, depending on the degree of compression of the adsorbed film.

It is generally desirable to calibrate or at least compare solution adsorption methods against gas adsorption, as was successfully illustrated by Smith and Hurley (53) for adsorption on activated carbon. Yet, when only relative surface areas are desired, this may not be necessary.

Many adsorbents have been used, but it appears that the organic molecules have been more popular, for example, acetic acid or dyes. In the latter case, it is possible to measure spectrophotometrically the concentration of the dye in the solution.

## CHANGE IN ELECTROLYTIC RESISTIVITY (COULTER COUNTER) (54)

This method determines a number-volume particle size distribution of particles suspended in an electrically conductive liquid. The suspension flows through a small aperture having an immersed electrode on either side. The particle concentration is made low enough that the particles traverse the aperture one at a time in most cases (55, 56).

Each particle passage displaces electrolyte within the aperture, momentarily changing the resistance between the electrodes and producing a voltage pulse, presumably proportional to particle *volume*. The resulting series of pulses is amplified, scaled, and counted using pulse-height analysis.

In order to have the Coulter Counter response proportional to size, a highly conducting medium is required, about $0.1M$ electrolyte. In some instances this type of medium may interact with and/or solvate the particles and alter their size-to-voltage response ratio. For phosphates and flour below 40 microns deviations of Coulter Counter data from sedimentation, microscopy, and sieving have been reported (57, 58). These deviations are probably due to the dependence of the response of the Coulter Counter on physical chemical properties of particulate matter other than particle volume. On the other hand, The

Coulter Counter has been found satisfactory on particles that have a chemically inert surface, for example, glass or plastic particles.

The size range of applicability for the Coulter Counter is hard to evaluate. The manufacturer claims a range of 0.5 to 500 microns, whereas up to now no completely satisfactory data have been reported below 5 microns and above 100 microns. Considering the relatively high price of the equipment, about $5000, The Coulter Counter is being utilized only in scattered applications.

## CASCADE IMPACTOR FOR AIR-BORNE PARTICLES

The stability and effectiveness of aerosols and sprays depends in many cases on the particle size distribution of the suspended matter. Impingement devices have been used for many years as a method of sampling gas-borne particles, including aerosols. In some cases (59–61) a single dry glass slide was used to collect samples of gas particulate suspended in a gaseous medium and the sizes of impacted particles were measured with a microscope by laborious particle counts. In May's cascade system of impactor stages (62) particles were separated into five fractions ranging in particle size from 1 to 50 microns. Brink (63) gives a comprehensive list of other references on the history, theory and development of impingement devices.

The normal particle size of air-borne particles lies in the range of 0.1–100 microns. During the last few years, two designs of impingement devices, called cascade impactors, became available that made the rapid and accurate measurements of air-borne particles in this size range feasible. One unit, designed and checked by Brink, covers the range of 0.2–5 microns and has been successfully used at plants throughout the country on gases saturated with vapors (aerosols) at 30°–200° C. The other unit, designed by Mitchell and Pilcher (64), is applicable in the range of 2–100 microns. Both units can be used on either solid or liquid particles to measure such things as air pollutants, commercial aerosols, or cigarette smoke. A quick method for drop size measurement of hollow-cone sprays has also been described (65).

A cascade impactor for measuring particle sizes is normally constructed of a succession of jets, each followed by an impaction slide. It is based on the principle that particles in a moving air stream impact on a slide placed in their path, if their momentum is sufficient to overcome the drag exerted by the air stream as it moves around the slide. Since each jet is designed to be smaller than the previous one, the velocity of the air stream and therefore that of the dispersed particles are increased as the aerosol advances through the impactor. Eventually

## TABLE 8-2
### Techniques for Determination of Particle Size Distribution in Aerosols*

| Measurement of Particle Sizes | Measurement of Corresponding Concentrations | Limitations of Method |
| --- | --- | --- |
| I. Use of microscope or electron microscope to measure the diameter of particles precipitated on a slide by (1) gravitational sedimentation, (2) directed flow, (3) thermal precipitation, or (4) electrostatic precipitation. | Use of microscope or electron microscope to count number of particles of each size present in a given sample. | Tedious and time consuming, since many particles should be measured and counted. The assumption that all particles from a given volume are caught on the slide is not always justified. |
| II. Sedimentation based on Stokes' law. A. Gravitational settling. Settling distance as a function of time. For small particles precautions against convection should be taken. | Different analytical methods. Aa.[1] Cumulative weight of particles precipitated on a sedimentation balance as a function of time. Ab.[2] Total intensity of transmitted or scattered light as a function of time. Ac.[3] Electric current from precipitated charged particles as a function of time. | Only relatively large particles (1–22-micron radius) can be considered.  Absolute size distribution of very heterogeneous aerosols cannot be determined. Ac1. Limitation is determined by the sensibility of the micro-microammeter. Ac2. The sedimentation time is very long for small particles. |
| B. Centrifugal sedimentation. Settling distance as a function of time for a given set of parameters (angular velocity, dimensions of apparatus, etc.) | Ba.[4] Weight of samples taken at different times or at different radii of rotation. Only suspensions in liquids are used. Bb.[5] Microscopic counting of particles on a slide, or quantitative chemical analysis of particles placed on certain portions of a slide. Bc.[2] Electric current from charged particles precipitated on the conducting bottom as a function of time. | Size distribution of the particles can be determined only if the particles are suspended in liquids.  See limitations under I. A very low flow rate of aerosol is required.  See limitations under IIAc; besides, (1) Reynold's number should be less than 1, (2) $w^2r$ must be much larger than $g$. |
| C. Electrostatic precipitation. Distance traveled by a charged particle as a function of time. | Ca.[6] Electric current from the plate where particles of a given size are precipitated. Cb.[7] Electric current in a precipitator as a function of time. | See IIAc1. All particles charged by diffusion will precipitate in the same place. |
| III. Cascade impactor. Particles in a given size range can be separated at a given velocity. | Weight of particles on successive slides, quantitative chemical analysis of these particles, or counting them on successive slides.[8] | Only a rough estimate of size distribution is possible. |
| IV. Optical densities of particle images as a function of particle radii. | Counting the number of particle images of given optical densities on a photoplate.[9] | See I. Radii should be a single valued function of intensity. The apparatus needs calibration with particles of given optical properties. |
| V. A.[10] Electric pulses produced by charged particles hitting a wire connected to the grid of an amplifier as a function of particle size. B.[11] Electric pulses produced in a photomultiplier by light scattered by individual particles as a function of particle size. | Counting pulses of given amplitudes.  Counting pulses of given amplitudes. | Only relatively large particles can be measured (>100 microns).  The apparatus needs calibration with particles of given optical properties. The apparatus is very expensive. |
| VI. Angle-dependent scattering intensity as a function of particle size (Mie or diffraction theory).[12] | Total intensity of scattered light as a function of angle of observation. | Size distribution of a mixture consisting only of two monodisperse fractions of aerosol can be determined. |

## TABLE 8-2 (Notes)

* Reproduced from V. G. Drozier and V. K. La Mer, *J. Colloid Sci.*, **14**, 74 (1959) by permission from the authors.

[1] S. Oden, *Colloid Chemistry*, Vol. I, ed. by J. Alexander, Chemical Catalog Co., New York, 1926.

[2] (a) ABC, *Handbook on Aerosols*, Washington, D. C., 1950. (b) V. K. La Mer, J. Benedict, G. G. Goyer, and J. Kruger, *Progress Reports on Contract AF-19 (122)-164 (1951)*. (c) M. Kerker, A. Lucile Cox, and M. D. Shoenberg, *J. Colloid Sci.*, **10**, 413 (1955).

[3] It is possible to apply a centrifugal or gravitational field instead of an electrostatic field in the precipitator. In these cases, Stokes' law would give an even stronger dependence between time of falling and particle size. These two methods, however, would be more difficult to handle experimentally.

[4] C. Brown, *J. Phys. Chem.*, **48**, 246 (1944); M. E. Robinson and S. W. Martin, *J. Phys. Chem.*, **52**, 854 (1948); H. J. Kamak, *Anal. Chem.*, **23**, 844 (1951).

[5] K. F. Sawyer and W. H. Walton, *Rev. Sci. Instr.*, **27**, 272 (1950).

[6] H. Rohman, *Z. Physik*, **17**, 253 (1923); S. N. Fuchs, I. Petryanov, and B. Rotzeig, *Trans. Faraday Soc.*, **32**, 1131 (1936); W. N. Lipscome, T. R. Rubin, and T. N. Sturdivant, *J. Appl. Phys.*, **18**, 72 (1947); J. H. Daniel and I. S. Bracket, *J. Appl. Phys.*, **22**, 542 (1951).

[7] V. G. Drozin and V. K. La Mer, *J. Colloid Sci.*, **14**, 74 (1959).

[8] K. R. May, *J. Sci. Instr.*, **22**, 187 (1945); L. S. Sonkin, *J. Ind. Hyg. Toxicol.*, **28**, 269 (1946); R. M. Ferry et al., *Chem. Rev.*, **44**, 389 (1949).

[9] P. K. Lee and V. K. La Mer, *Rev. Sci. Instr.*, **25**, 1004 (1954).

[10] A. C. Guyton, *J. Ind. Hyg. Toxicol.*, **28**, 133 (1946); F. T. Gucker, Jr., and C. T. O'Konski, *Chem. Rev.*, **44**, 373 (1949); T. U. Geist, T. L. York, and G. G. Bard Brown, *Ind. Eng. Chem.*, **43**, 1371 (1951).

[11] C. T. O'Konski and G. J. Doyle, *Tech. Rept. No. 1*, Contract ONR 222 (1954).

[12] M. Kerker and V. K. La Mer, *J. Am. Chem. Soc.*, **72**, 3516 (1950).

particles with sufficient inertia impact against a cup or a slide and are collected. After the run, the sample slides or cups are removed and the quantity collected is determined either by weighing or by chemical analysis.

Before a cascade impactor can be used for particle size analysis, it must be calibrated (64) to determine the size of particles that impact on each slide. The most accurate calibration procedure is that of microscopic measurement. The calibration is sensitive to the geometry of the cascade impaction, gas flow rate, density of the particles, and temperature.

## LIGHT SCATTERING AS A MEASURE OF PARTICLE SIZE

The light-scattering technique is based on the fact that illuminated particles serve as secondary radiation sources in a manner which is related to their size.

When the size of suspended particles is very small with respect to the wavelength of light, or when the refractive index of the particles is very close to that of the medium, the relatively simple equations of Rayleigh (66) and Rayleigh and Gans (67), respectively, can be used.

The first condition is generally valid in molecular-weight determinations on polymeric materials. Except for special circumstances or special systems, neither condition is fulfilled in colloidal solutions or microsopic suspensions. Therefore, it is necessary, in general, to have recourse to the Mie theory (68), which contains the restrictive conditions that the particles be spherical and intrinsically isotropic.

The Mie theory, however, is so complex even for monodisperse systems that its application to polydisperse systems has not been practical because of the magnitude of the calculation problem. With the advent of electronic computers, the task has become somewhat easier, and several tabulations of Mie functions have become available (69).

If the light-scattering systems are not monodisperse, that is, not all the particles are the same size, the particle size obtained from light-scattering measurements will represent an average value, related to but not identical with the weight-average particle size. These averages are bound to differ with the shapes of the particles, the particle size distribution, and the degree of nonisotropy.

Heller (69) was able to evaluate the particle size distribution of heterodisperse polystyrene lattices whose particles are spherical and isotropic. He had to assume a priori, however, the particle size distribution function.

Sloan (70) found that the simpler, more restrictive Rayleigh-Gans theory (67) serves fairly well as an approximation to the more complex Mie theory treatment. Gaddy (71) used this approach to obtain rapid estimation of moderator turbidity particle size in heavy-water reactors.

Because of the difficulties we have outlined, the utilization of light scattering for particle size distribution measurements has been limited to special systems, and more specifically to aerosols.

Aerosols are suspensions of generally spherical and isotropic liquid droplets in a gaseous phase. In addition, the size distribution is usually narrow so that an average size is meaningful, and the particles are below 10 microns. These factors are especially attractive for light scattering, particularly since the conventional methods for particle size distribution measurements, for example, sedimentation, are not applicable.

Several authoritative review articles are available on light-scattering theory and instrumentation, designed specifically for aerosols, and interested readers are referred to them (72–78).

A commercial instrument based on light scattering for measuring a particle size distribution of aerosols has become available recently (79). Aerosol particles in a suitable stream are passed through the sensing region of an optical system. This region is intensely illuminated by means of a light source. Particles entering it scatter incident light, a fraction of which proceeds to a photomultiplier tube. Since the particles traverse the illuminated region in a few milliseconds, the electrical signals at the photomultiplier appear in the form of pulses. These are sent on to an electronic pulse-height analyzer for pulse amplitude analysis. Although it has not yet been demonstrated that the data represent absolute size values, changes in aerosols are readily detected.

**REFERENCES**

1. W. J. Marculaitis, *J. Colloid Sci.*, **12**, 581 (1957).
2. R. C. Cadle, *Particle Size Determination,* Interscience Publishers, New York, 1955, p. 293; Sales Data 50–250, Sperry Products Co., Danbury, Conn.
3. F. S. Sinnat and L. Slater, *Fuel,* **2,** 142 (1932).
4. H. E. Rose, *The Measurement of Particle Size in Very Fine Powders,* Chemical Publishing Co., New York, 1954.
5. J. J. Hermans, *Flow Properties of Disperse Systems,* North-Holland Publishing Co., Amsterdam, 1953.
6. P. W. Selwood, *Magnetochemistry,* Interscience Publishers, New York, 1956, second edition, pp. 91, 122–126, 389–396.
7. F. G. Drozin and V. K. La Mer, *J. Colloid Sci.,* **14,** 74 (1959).
8. N. E. Lloyd, *ibid.,* **14,** 441 (1959).
9. A. Kahn and D. R. Lewis, *J. Phys. Chem.,* **58,** 801 (1954).
10. H. Benoit, *Ann. Phys.,* **6,** 561 (1951).

11. C. T. O'Konski and B. Zimm, *Science,* **11**, 113 (1950).
12. R. L. Dimmick, M. T. Hatch, and J. Ng, *A.M.A. Arch. Ind. Health,* **18**, 23 (1958).
13. J. M. Dallavalle, *Micromeritics,* Pitman Publishing Corp., New York, second edition, 1948, Chapter 13.
14. P. C. Carman, *J. Soc. Chem. Ind. (London),* **57**, 225 (1938).
15. ———, *Flow of Gases through Porous Media,* Butterworths, London, 1956.
16. R. R. Sullivan and K. L. Hertel, *J. Appl. Phys.,* **11**, 761 (1940).
17. J. L. Fowler and K. L. Hertel, *ibid.,* **11**, 496 (1940).
18. P. C. Carman, *J. Soc. Chem. Ind. (London),* **58**, 1 (1939).
19. E. L. Gooden and C. M. Smith, *Ind. Eng. Chem. (Anal. Ed.),* **12**, 497 (1940).
20. F. B. Hutto and D. W. Davis, *Offic. Dig. Federation Paint Varnish Prod. Clubs,* **31**, 429 (1959).
21. R. L. Blaine, *ASTM Bull.,* **108**, 17 (1941).
22. S. S. Ober and K. J. Frederick, *ASTM Spec. Tech. Publ. No. 234,* p. 279, (1958).
23. A. Pechukas and F. W. Gage, *Ind. Eng. Chem.,* **18**, 370 (1946).
24. P. C. Carman and P. R. Malherbe, *J. Soc. Chem. Ind. (London),* **69**, 134 (1950).
25. ———, *J. Appl. Chem. (London),* **1**, 105 (1951).
26. R. M. Barrer and D. M. Grove, *Trans. Faraday Soc.,* **47**, 826 (1951).
27. G. Kraus and J. W. Ross, *J. Phys. Chem.,* **57**, 330 (1953).
28. B. V. Deryagin, *Compt. Rend. Acad. Sci. U.R.S.S.,* **53**, 623 (1946).
29. C. G. Dogg, J. W. Davis, and F. D. Pidgeon, *J. Phys. Coll. Chem.,* **55**, 684 (1951).
30. R. T. Johansen, P. B. Lorenz, C. G. Dodd, F. D. Pidgeon, and J. W. Davis, *J. Phys. Chem.,* **57**, 40 (1953).
31. R. R. Sullivan, *J. Appl. Phys.,* **13**, 728 (1942).
32. E. J. Wiggins, W. B. Cambell, and O. Maass, *Can. J. Research,* **17B**, 318 (1939).
33. J. A. Allen and C. J. Haigh, *J. Chem. Educ.,* **31**, 354 (1954).
34. R. R. Irani, C. F. Callis, and T. Liu, *Ind. Eng. Chem.,* **51**, 1285 (1959).
35. R. R. Irani, H. L. Vandersall, and W. W. Morgenthaler, *ibid.,* **53**, 141 (1961).
36. R. B. Anderson and P. H. Emmett, *J. Appl. Phys.,* **19**, 367 (1948).
37. S. Brunauer, *The Adsorption of Gases and Vapors,* Vol. I, Princeton University Press, Princeton, N. J., 1945.
38. N. K. Adam, *The Physics and Chemistry of Surfaces,* third edition, Oxford University Press, London, 1941.
39. A. W. Adamson, *Physical Chemistry of Surfaces,* Interscience Publishers, New York, 1960.
40. K. J. Mysels, *Introduction to Colloid Chemistry,* Interscience Publishers, New York, 1959.
41. J. Fries, "The Determination of Particle Size by Adsorption Methods," *ASTM Spec. Tech. Publ. No. 234,* 1958.
42. C. Orr and J. M. Dallavalle, *Fine Particle Measurement,* The Macmillan Company, New York, 1959.
43. P. H. Emmett, *ASTM Spec. Tech. Publ. No. 51,* 1941.
44. J. W. McBain and A. M. Bakr, *J. Am. Chem. Soc.,* **48**, 690 (1926).
45. W. O. Milligan, W. C. Simpson, G. L. Bushey, H. H. Rachford, and A. L. Draper, *Anal. Chem.,* **23**, 739 (1951).
46. H. B. Klevens, J. T. Carriel, R. J. Fries, and A. H. Peterson, *The Proceedings*

of the Second International Congress of Surface Activity, Butterworths, London, 1957.

47. F. M. Nelsen and F. T. Eggersten, *Anal. Chem.*, **30**, 1387 (1958).

48. S. Brunauer, P. H. Emmett, and E. Teller, *J. Am. Chem. Soc.*, **60**, 309 (1938).

49. J. R. Goates and C. V. Hatch, *Soil Sci.*, **75**, 275 (1953).

50. S. Glasstone, *Physical Chemistry*, second edition, D. Van Nostrand Co., New York, 1946, p. 1217.

51. I. Langmuir, *J. Am. Chem. Soc.*, **38**, 2221 (1916); **39**, 1885 (1917); **40**, 1361 (1918).

52. D. Graham and R. S. Hansen, *J. Phys. Chem.*, **60**, 1153 (1956).

53. H. A. Smith and R. B. Hurley, *J. Phys. and Colloid Chem.*, **6**, 443 (1951).

54. Coulter Industrial Sales Co., P. O. Box 22, Elmhurst, Ill.

55. R. H. Berg, *ASTM Spec. Tech. Publ. 234*, p. 245 (1959).

56. H. E. Kubitschek, *Res. Appl. Ind.*, **13**, 128 (1960).

57. R. R. Irani, *Anal. Chem.*, **32**, 1162 (1960).

58. E. S. Palik, *ibid.*, **33**, 956 (1961).

59. T. Hatch, H. Warren, and P. Drinker, *J. Ind. Hyg. Toxicol.*, **14**, 301 (1932).

60. J. S. Owens, *Proc. Roy. Soc. (London)*, **A101**, 18 (1922).

61. R. M. Ferry, L. E. Farr, and M. G. Hartmann, *Chem. Rev.*, **44**, 389 (1949).

62. J. R. May, *J. Sci. Instr.*, **22**, 187 (1945).

63. J. A. Brink, *Ind. Eng. Chem.*, **50**, 645 (1958).

64. R. I. Mitchell and J. M. Pilcher, *ibid.*, **51**, 1039 (1959).

65. H. Binark and W. E. Ranz, *Ind. Eng. Chem.*, **51**, 701 (1959).

66. Lord Rayleigh, *Phil. Mag.*, **12**, 81 (1881).

67. ———, *Proc. Roy. Soc. (London)*, **A84**, 25 (1911); **A90**, 219 (1914); R. Gans, *Ann. Physik.*, **76**, 29 (1925).

68. G. Mie, *Ann. D. Physik.*, **25**, 377 (1908).

69. W. Heller, *Second Conference on Analytical Chemistry in Nuclear Reactor Technology*, Gatlinburg, Tenn., Oct. 1958, TIS issuance date, April, 1959, Oak Ridge National Lab., Oak Ridge, Tenn.

70. C. K. Sloan, *J. Phys. Chem.*, **59**, 834 (1955).

71. R. H. Gaddy, *Third Conference on Analytical Chemistry in Nuclear Reactor Technology*, Gatlinburg, Tenn., Oct. 1959.

72. C. T. O'Konski, M. D. Bitron, W. I. Higuski, *ASTM Spec. Tech. Publ. No. 234*, p. 180 (1958).

73. D. Sinclair and V. K. LaMer, *Chem. Rev.*, **44**, 245 (1949).

74. W. Heller, J. N. Epel, and R. M. Tabibian, *J. Chem. Phys.*, **22**, 1777 (1954).

75. D. Sinclair, *Handbook of Aerosols*, Atomic Energy Commission, Washington, D. C., 1950, Chapters 7 and 8.

76. R. M. Tabibian and W. Heller, *J. Coll. Sci.*, **13**, 6 (1958).

77. R. Tabibian, W. Heller, and J. N. Epel, *ibid.*, **11**, 195 (1956).

78. Also see Symposium on Aerosols, published in *Chem. Rev.*, **44**, 245–389 (1949).

79. Particle Counter Model PC-200A, Royco Instruments, Inc., 440 Olive Street, Palo Alto, Calif. Cost approximately $7000.

# chapter 9

# Comparison of particle size distribution data from various methods

The introduction of new techniques and the modification of older techniques for measurement of the particle size distribution have increased over the last few years, as is evident from previous chapters. The increase is due to the increased need for better characterization of powdered and granular materials.

When a specific method is to be adopted, it is important to compare the data with those obtained by other methods, particularly if one of these methods had been previously proven to be reliable. In making particle size distribution comparisons, however, we should express the distributions on the same basis, for example, number-size or weight-size distribution.

Since the majority of powdered and granular materials include particles that deviate from sphericity, the working definition of size that was presented in Chapter 2 is highly important.

In this chapter the results from several methods are discussed and intercompared. Because size is a linear dimension, direct particle size measurements utilizing a linear scale, with or without a microscope, should give the most indisputable results. The major disadvantage of direct methods has been the excessive time that had to be spent per determination, measuring hundreds of particles to assure representative sampling. Now, however, the development of electronic counters and sizers (which are still relatively expensive) has eliminated this objection almost completely by shortening the time required per determination to a few minutes.

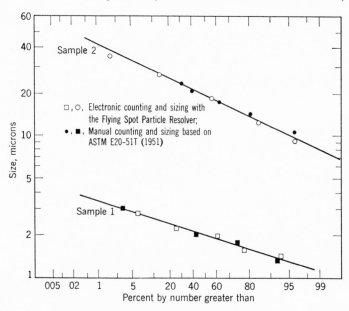

FIG. 9-1. Agreement between electronic and manual microscopic counting on two apatite sands.

Therefore, whenever possible, particle-sizing techniques should be compared with microscopy. Figure 9-1 demonstrates that electronic and manual microscopic counting and sizing give equivalent results. Table 9-1 shows that microscopic electronic counting and sizing and

TABLE 9-1

Comparison of Particle Size Distribution Data from Microscopy and Sedimentation Balance (1)

| Material | Dispersion Fluid | Geometric Mean Size $M_g$ (microns) | | Geometric Standard Deviation $\sigma_g$ | |
|---|---|---|---|---|---|
| | | Micro-scopy | Sedimen-tation | Micro-scopy | Sedimen-tation |
| Sand | Water | 20.7 | 21.2 | 1.96 | 2.00 |
| Glass beads | Butanol | 32.5 | 31.0 | 1.38 | 1.34 |
| Monocalcium phosphate | 2-Ethylhexanol | 71.5 | 70.0 | 3.54 | 3.50 |
| Tricalcium phosphate | Ethanol | 4.4 | 4.2 | 1.95 | 1.95 |
| Flour | Benzene | 57.0 | 58.0 | — | — |

the sedimentation balance method give equivalent particle size distributions when both are compared on the same basis, whether number-size or weight-size (1). This is in agreement with the work of Heiss and Coull (2), who found that the settling velocity of a chubby particle is surprisingly close to that of a sphere of equal volume. Therefore, if the ratio of the maximum to the minimum diameter does not exceed 3 (see Chapter 2), sedimentation methods should give results that agree within experimental error with those from microscopy, provided the limitations outlined in Chapter 5 for sedimentation are observed.

Figure 9-2 is an intercomparison (3) of two sedimentation balance methods, the Andreasen pipet method and microscopy, on two samples of hard wheat flour. The sedimentation balances are the automatized Gallenkamp balance described by Ames et al. (1), and the commercial Recording Sedibal, described in Chapter 5. Electronic counting and sizing was utilized in the microscopic determination. The intercomparison shows that the Andreasen pipet data deviated from the others for the finer flour sample, presumably because disturbance of the suspen-

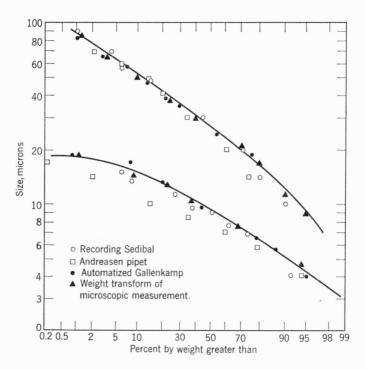

FIG. 9-2. Comparison of sedimentation balance, Andreasen pipet method, and microscopy on two flour samples.

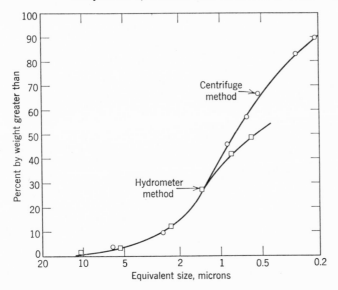

FIG. 9-3. Particle size data obtained with a sedimentation hydrometer and by a centrifuge method. See S. G. Maguire and G. W. Phelps, *J. Am. Ceram. Soc.*, **40**, 403 (1957).

sion occurred during sample withdrawal. The disturbance was probably not large enough to cause deviations for the coarse flour sample. On the other hand, Rabatin and Gale (4) found only a slight deviation between their sedimentation balance and the Andreasen pipet method.

Figure 9-3 is a comparison (5) of the hydrometer sedimentation method with a centrifuge method (6). The two methods are shown to agree surprisingly well in the size region of 2–10 microns; but, as expected, the failure of the hydrometer method in the colloidal region is obvious from the low readings it gives.

Sammarone and Saunders' comparison (7) between a modified hydrometer method (also known as the Westphall balance) and the Palo-Travis method is illustrated in Fig. 9-4. It is difficult to decide which one of these two methods is the more accurate. Nevertheless, these investigators claimed better precision for the Westphall balance method. They also claimed that the long distance of settling in the Palo-Travis method made the sedimentation experiments take 3–7 days for a pigment whose particles were in the size range of 2–44 microns; whereas the Westphall balance method required only about 2 hours.

Figure 9-5 illustrates that incomplete dispersion was attained when air sedimentation was utilized on a tungsten powder (8). For the liquid turbidimetric sedimentation method, the sample was dispersed with spatulation. In this same work (8) it was found that the Fisher Sub-Sieve Sizer (see Chapter 8) gave values that are comparable with those from air sedimentation.

Extensive work (9) on calcium and sodium phosphates showed that the Fisher Sub-Sieve Sizer readings are strongly influenced by the very fine end of the size distribution. No direct correlation with any sedimentation measurement was obtained. Hutto and Davis (10) confirmed these observations on silica gel. They intercompared sedimentation, BET sorption, and air permeability (Fisher Sub-Sieve Sizer). No two of the three methods agreed. Thus, the difference between BET sorption and sedimentation is due to the internal surface area included in the sorption measurement. Permeability methods were found to give values that are intermediate between sedimentation and sorption because they are affected by inside channels in the particles (11) but not by dead void space.

Anderson and Emmett (12) compared electron microscopy and low-

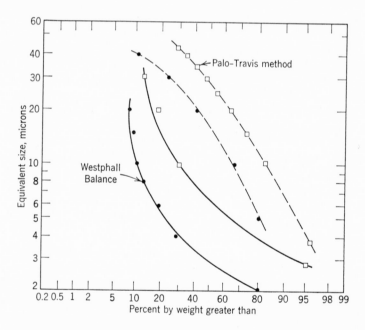

FIG. 9-4. Particle size distribution comparison on color oxides between a modified hydrometer method (Westphall Balance) and the Palo-Travis method. See D. G. Sammarone and H. S. Saunders, *Am. Ceram. Soc. Bull.*, **36**, 340 (1957). The dashed line and the solid line represent two different samples.

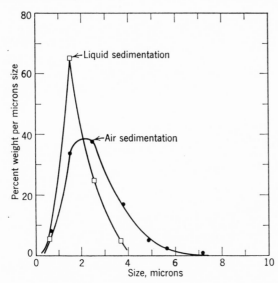

FIG. 9-5. Comparison of particle size distribution on tungsten powder using air sedimentation (Micromerograph) and a turbidimetric liquid sedimentation method. See A. I. Michaels, T. L. Weaver, and R. C. Nelson, *ASTM Bull. No. 247,* p. 140 (1960).

temperature nitrogen adsorption for measuring the particle size of carbon black in the size range of 0.01–0.02 micron. For nonporous carbon black samples, the two techniques agreed within 8%, certainly within experimental error. Porous carbon black samples gave a calculated lower apparent particle size from adsorption than from electron microscopy because of the inclusion of internal surface area in the adsorption measurements.

In Fig. 9-6, microscopy, gravitational sedimentation, centrifugal sedimentation, micromesh sieving, and changes in electrolytic resistivity (the Coulter Counter) are intercompared for measurement of the particle size distribution of two samples of flour (13). Except for the Coulter Counter method, all these methods agree with one another within experimental error. The deviation of the Coulter Counter from the established microscopic and sedimentation methods has also been observed by Irani (14) and Palik (15). For some coarse materials, for example, flour, The Coulter Counter technique can be calibrated with the more accurate methods. For materials with 100% of the particles below 15 microns, however, for example, tricalcium phosphate, no agreement whatsoever could be found between the Coulter Counter

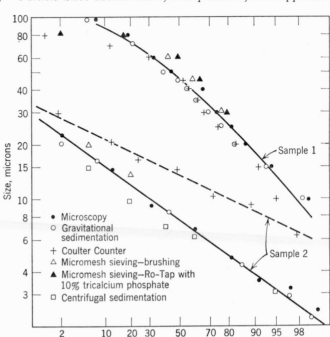

FIG. 9-6. Intercomparison of methods for the particle size distribution measurement of flour.

and the other techniques. This disagreement is probably due to the dependence of the response of the Coulter Counter on physical chemical properties other than size (14, 15).

As can be noted from Figs. 9-6 and 9-7, calibrated micromesh sieves can be utilized on powders with geometric mean sizes as low as 6 microns (13, 16). Woven sieves cannot be utilized down in this range. For powders with more than 80% of the particles larger than 44 microns (325-mesh woven United States sieve), the particle size distribution as determined by woven sieves is accurate, as illustrated in Fig. 9-8. Figure 9-9, previously discussed in Chapter 7, demonstrates that when more than 35% of the particles by weight are below 325 mesh, woven-sieve analysis is inaccurate and fails to show significant differences between samples. This failure is probably due to the deformation of woven sieves on use. Obviously, these deformations become serious for mesh openings of about 275 or finer.

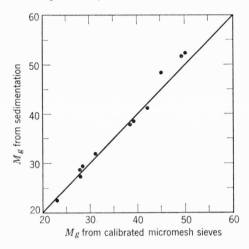

FIG. 9-7. Agreement between calibrated micromesh sieves and sedimentation for several calcium phosphates: $M_g$ is the geometric mean size on a weight basis in microns.

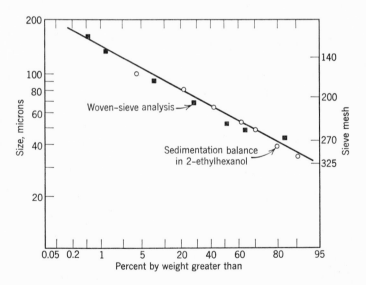

FIG. 9-8. The particle size distribution of a sodium isethionate sample. See D. P. Ames, R. R. Irani, and C. F. Callis, *J. Phys. Chem.*, **63**, 531 (1959).

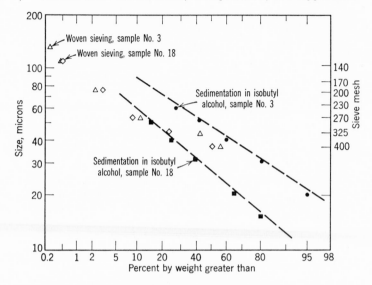

FIG. 9-9. The comparison between woven-sieve analysis and the more accurate methods on anhydrous monocalcium phosphate. Microscopy data converted to weight are represented by the dashed lines.

Wichser and Shellenberger's intercomparison (17) of sieving, liquid sedimentation (Andreasen pipet), and air flotation (Roller Air Analyzer (18)) on flour is illustrated in Fig. 9-10. It was concluded that sieving is applicable above 37 microns, air flotation below 80 microns, and the Andreasen pipet below 50 microns.

Work at the Oak Ridge National Laboratory (19) on thorium oxide in the particle size range of 0.2–20 microns established that centrifugal sedimentation data correlate well with results obtained by gravitational sedimentation methods (Andreasen pipet, turbidimetric, and activation analysis) for the portion of sample composed of particulate matter greater than 2 microns in size. The results on one representative sample are shown in Fig. 9-11. In the majority of tests made, thorium oxide was found to exhibit no significant difference in particle size distribution when the sedimentation tests were made in different dispersing media. This was not always the case, however, and indeed when $0.005M$ $H_2SO_4$ was utilized as the dispersing medium, the measured particle size distribution differed considerably from that when either xylene or $0.005M$ $Na_4P_2O_7$ was utilized.

In the size range below 10 microns, it has been repeatedly shown (20) that, if proper dispersion is achieved, centrifugal sedimentation utilizing the layer technique (see Chapter 5) and the electron microscope

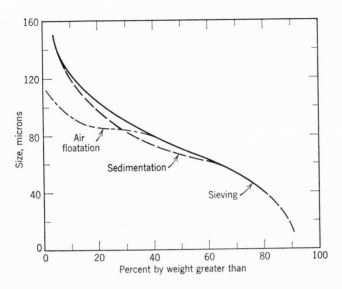

FIG. 9-10. Comparison of particle size distribution curves for wheat flour by sieving, air flotation (Roller Analyzer), and sedimentation (Andreasen pipet). See F. W. Wichser and J. A. Shellenberger, *Cereal Chem.*, **25**, 155 (1948).

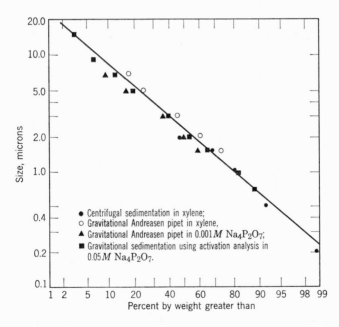

FIG. 9-11. Particle size distribution of thorium oxide. Comparison of centrifugal and gravitational methods using various dispersing media. See O. Menis, H. P. House, and C. M. Boyd, *ORNL-2345*, Chemistry-General.

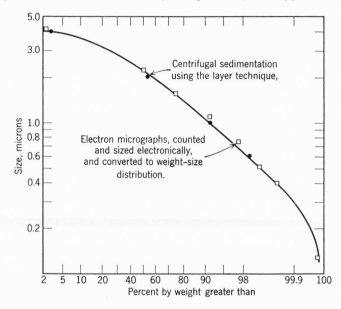

FIG. 9-12. Intercomparison of electron microscopy and centrifugal sedimentation on silica.

data (counted and sized electronically) gave identical particle size distributions. This is illustrated in Fig. 9-12 for measurements on silica powder. Agreement between light microscopy and centrifugal sedimentation has also been noted by Whitby (21).

Batel (22) made a thorough investigation of sieving, air separation, sedimentation, and the Blaine permeameter (23). He concluded that sieving is strongly affected by the sieving motion, especially when a large fraction is present below 60 microns. Air separation using the B.A.H.C.O. Classifier (see reference 104 in Chapter 5) was found to be useful in the 30–100-micron range. The Blaine permeameter was found to give characteristic numbers that did not correspond to particle size by itself. If the particles are properly dispersed, it was concluded that sedimentation (Andreasen pipet) is useful in the 1–60-micron range.

A critical comparison (24) of the Andreasen pipet and sedimentation balance (Recording Sedibal) methods showed the latter to be more precise and to require less manpower for operation.

## Summary

It has been established that if microscopy, gravitational sedimentation using a balance, centrifugal sedimentation using the layer technique, and sieving are utilized in their proper particle size ranges (discussed in the next chapter), equivalent particle size distributions are obtained, independent of technique. The work of various investigators suggests that the more specialized particle size distribution techniques should only be utilized after they have been checked against the established methods.

In the next chapter, on recommended methods, the utilization of the established techniques for particle size distribution measurements are discussed in greater detail.

**REFERENCES**

1. D. P. Ames, R. R. Irani, and C. F. Callis, *J. Phys. Chem.*, **63**, 531 (1959).
2. J. F. Heiss and J. J. Coull, *J. Chem. Eng. Progr.*, **48**, 133 (1952).
3. R. R. Irani, unpublished results, Monsanto Chemical Co., St. Louis 66, Mo.
4. J. G. Rabatin and R. H. Gale, *Anal. Chem.*, **28**, 1314 (1956).
5. S. G. Maguire and G. W. Phelps, *J. Am. Ceram. Soc.*, **40**, 403 (1957).
6. S. W. Martin, *Ceram. Abstr.*, **21**, 92 (1942).
7. D. G. Sammarone and H. S. Saunders, *Am. Ceram. Soc. Bull.*, **36**, 340 (1957).
8. A. I. Michaels, T. L. Weaver, and R. C. Nelson, *ASTM Bull. No. 247*, p. 140 (1960).
9. J. C. Barnett and R. R. Irani, unpublished results, Monsanto Chemical Co., St. Louis 66, Mo.
10. F. B. Hutto and D. W. Davis, *Offic. Dig. Federation Paint Varnish Prod. Clubs*, **31**, 429 (1959).
11. D. H. Matthews, *J. Appl. Chem.*, **7**, 610 (1957).
12. R. B. Anderson and P. H. Emmett, *J. Appl. Phys.*, **19**, 367 (1948).
13. R. R. Irani and W. S. Fong, *Cereal Chem.*, **38**, 67 (1961).
14. R. R. Irani, *Anal. Chem.*, **32**, 1162 (1960).
15. E. S. Palik, *Anal. Chem.*, **33**, 956 (1961).
16. R. R. Irani and C. F. Callis, *Anal. Chem.*, **31**, 2026 (1959).
17. F. W. Wichser and J. A. Shellenberger, *Cereal Chem.*, **25**, 155 (1948).
18. *Particle Size Analysis of Metal Powders*, Metals Disintegrating Company, Elizabeth, N. J., 1946.
19. O. Menis, H. P. House, and C. M. Boyd, *ORNL-2345*, Chemistry-General, Office of Technical Services, U. S. Dept. of Commerce, Washington 25, D. C.
20. R. R. Irani and E. F. Kaelble, *Anal. Chem.*, **33**, 1168 (1961).
21. K. T. Whitby, *Heating, Piping and Air Conditioning*, **61**, 449 (1955).
22. W. Batel, *Chem. Ing. Tech.*, **29**, 581 (1957).
23. The Blaine Permeameter is offered by Precision Scientific Co., Chicago, Ill.
24. D. Bachman and H. Gerstenberg, *Chem. Ind. Tech.*, **29**, 589 (1957).

# chapter 10

# Procedure for choosing the appropriate method of particle size measurement

Analysts frequently face the problem of having to decide which particle size method is the most applicable to their problem. Figures 10-1 to 10-6 are aids to the analyst in making his decision. The reader can refer back to the appropriate chapter for more details on each method. A few examples of how the procedure would work for two powders with all particles below 100 microns are given below.

A research engineer is assigned the problem of designing cyclones to remove or isolate the finer particles in different powdered materials. Therefore, he is interested in weight-size distributions of the powders with a precision of ±3% at any specified size. He finds that none of the products involved are held on a 140-mesh woven sieve. For one powdered product he is interested in, more than 60% of the material passes through a 325-mesh woven sieve. With micromesh sieves, he finds that only 10% of the powder passes through the 20-micron sieve. Therefore, he adopts Ro-Tap sieving of calibrated micromesh sieves with the aid of a flow-conditioning agent (see Chapter 7).

Another product with the same size characteristics is very hygroscopic, for example, ammonium perchlorate, and sieving is almost impossible. For this product he uses liquid sedimentation in an organic fluid that disperses ammonium perchlorate but does not dissolve it.

A pigment manufacturer has to supply powders with no particles over 10 microns. He is interested in a routine plant method good to ±5% for controlling the product. The weight-size distribution of one pigment with a weight-median size of 2–3 microns can be readily measured with a Mine Safety Appliance Co. layer sedimentation centrifuge, using an appropriate dispersing fluid. Another pigment is significantly finer in size and has a weight median size of 0.1–0.5 micron. For this latter pigment he probably has to invest in an electron microscope, if this is possible. Counting the electron photomicrographs manually to obtain number-size distribution is feasible but tedious. If money is available, he will buy an automatic counting and sizing device such as Cinema Television's (London) Flying Spot Particle Resolver.

If the pigments are nonporous and have a smooth surface and only an average particle size is desired, the pigment manufacturer should seriously consider gaseous or liquid adsorption for surface area measurement.

The adoption of one specific method in preference to another must be based on such things as precision and accuracy required, cost of equipment, time per analysis, and caliber of personnel running the experiments.

Finally, it should be emphasized that we should measure the size attribute that is most directly correlated with the characteristic of interest and then keep the expression of size in those terms, unless comparisons outside the system are required. Table 10-1 shows the dimensions on which different measurement techniques are directly dependent.

**TABLE 10-1**

Dimensional Effects of Different Measurement Techniques[a]

| Distribution Weighting | Distribution Moment (Power of Distribution Variable) | | |
|---|---|---|---|
| | Size | Area | Volume |
| By number | Microscopy | Light scattering Turbidity | Coulter Counter |
| By area | — | | — |
| By volume | Sieving | All sedimentation methods and classifiers | — |

[a] Adapted from a private communication with Professor K. T. Whitby, University of Minnesota.

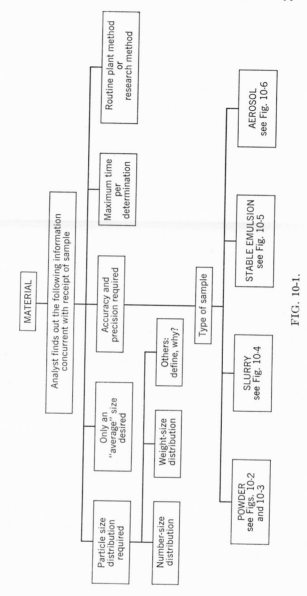

FIG. 10-1.

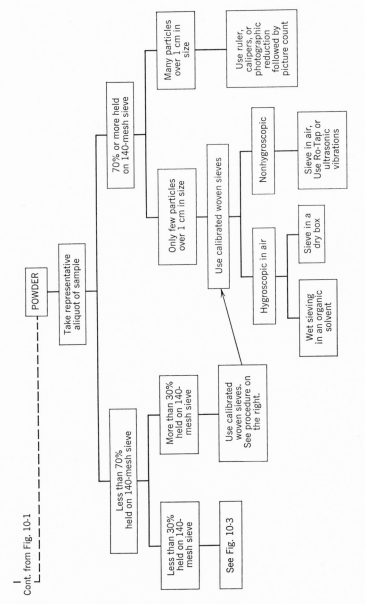

FIG. 10-2.

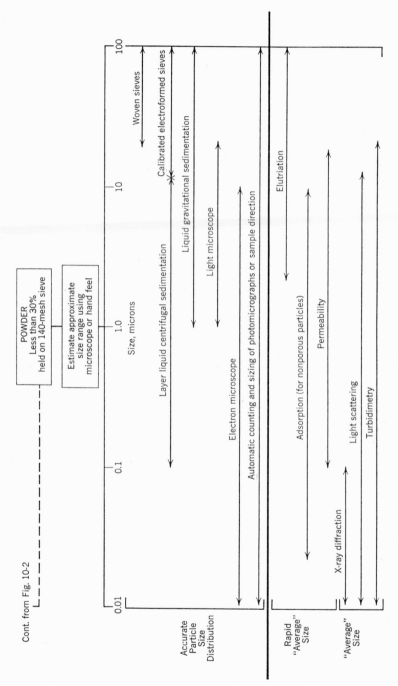

FIG. 10-3.

158

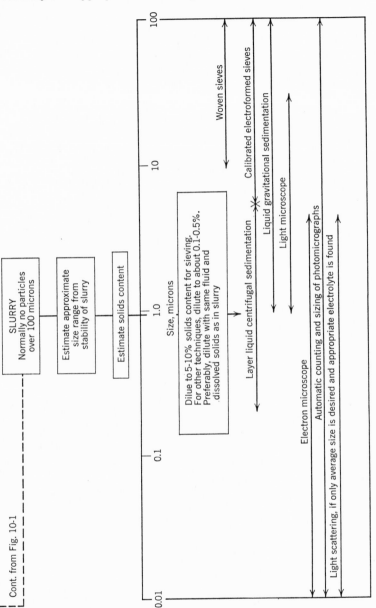

FIG. 10-4.

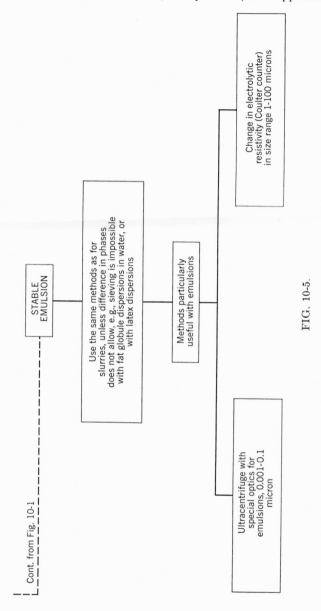

FIG. 10-5.

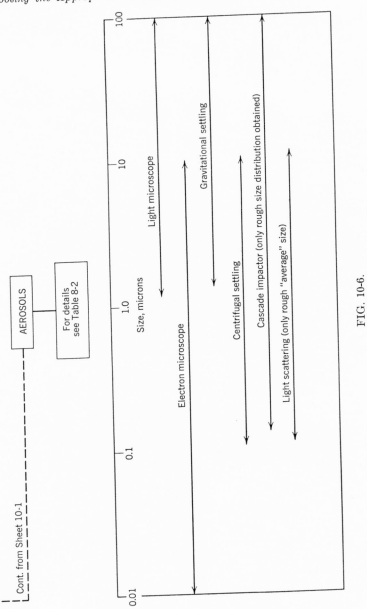

FIG. 10-6.

# Index

Italics indicate the page to which a literature reference pertains.